Age 3-5 English

I Can Learn

Mega English

EGMONT

We bring stories to life

First published in Great Britain in 2005 by Egmont UK Limited
239 Kensington High Street, London W8 6SA
Published in this edition in 2011

Activities by Brenda Apsley and Nina Filipek
Cover and interior illustrations by John Haslam

ISBN 978 1 4052 5893 7
1 3 5 7 9 10 8 6 4 2
Printed in Italy

Contents

Contents

About this book

Mega Reading and Writing 3–5 offers lots of practice in literacy skills as described in the Curriculum Guidance for the Foundation Stage. The book's content is in line with the recommendations of the National Curriculum for England and Wales and the National Guidelines for Scotland.

This book is divided into five main sections:

- **preparation for reading;**
- **identifying letter sounds (phonics);**
- **preparation for writing;**
- **reading simple words;**
- **writing the letters.**

Within these sections children will learn to:

1. **observe details in pictures;**
2. **scan the page from left to right;**
3. **say the sounds of the letters;**
4. **match sounds to pictures;**
5. **tell a simple story;**
6. **use a pencil confidently;**
7. **form the letters of the alphabet.**

The book is aimed at children aged 3 to 5, so the levels of the exercises are progressively more difficult. The content begins at Nursery level and moves up to Reception level. We recommend that your child works through the book in the given order. If they start to struggle or get bored with any of the pages, skip these activities and return to them on another day when your child is feeling more positive and responsive. Repetition and practice will help build skills and confidence.

Finding your way around

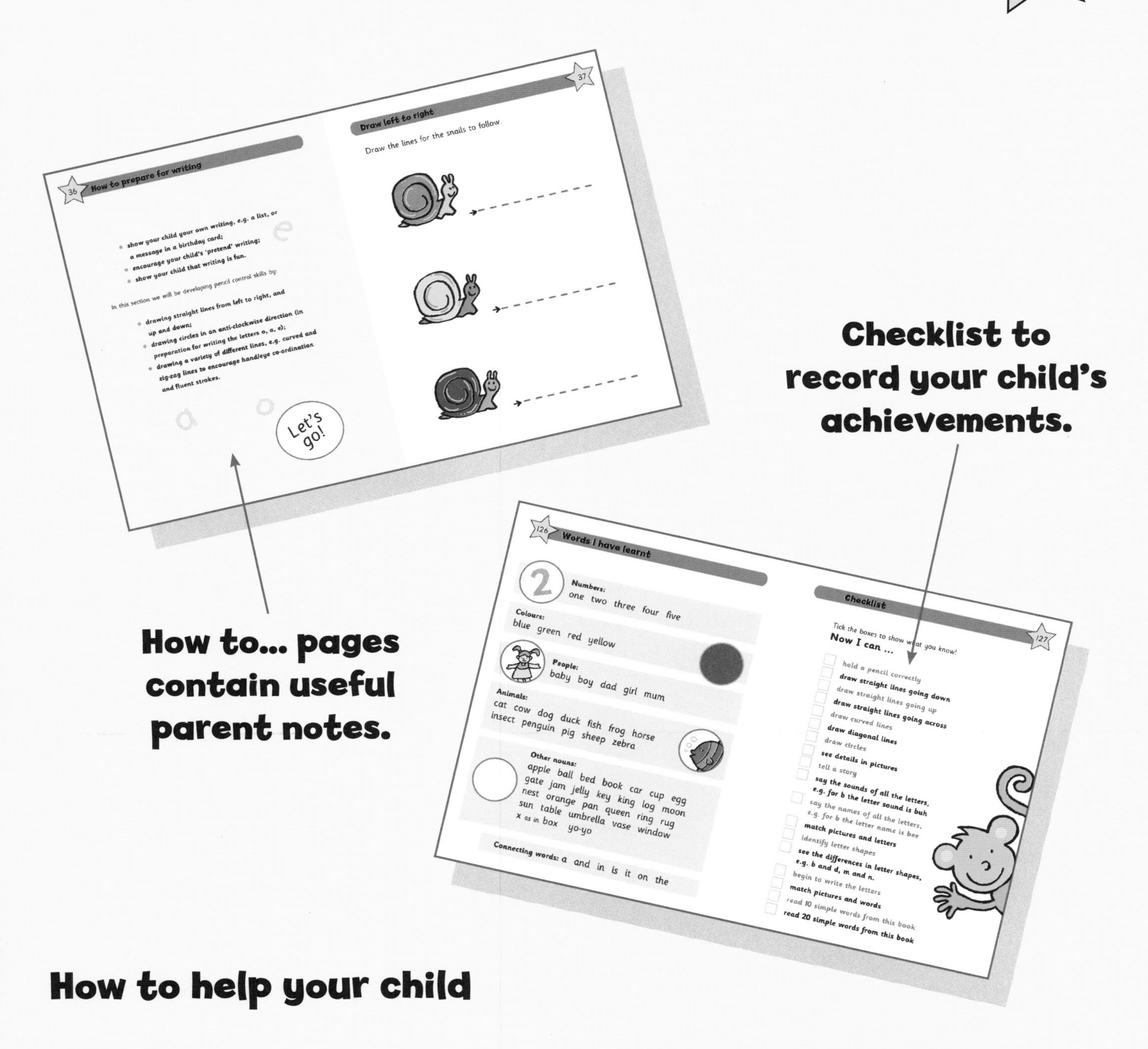

How to help your child

Choose a time when your child is alert and eager to learn. Read aloud and point to the instructions on each page. These are written using a simple vocabulary for the age group, but you may also need to explain more fully what your child is being asked to do. Make sure your child can hold a pencil correctly and let your child decide how they want to work on the book. Always give lots of encouragement and praise for effort and enjoy the book together.

How to prepare for reading

- ***make time for reading stories to your child;***
- ***show your child that you read yourself;***
- ***enjoy sharing songs and rhymes;***
- ***show your child that reading is fun.***

In preparation for reading, children need to learn to observe details: firstly, details in pictures and, later, details in words.

In this section, we will be developing observation skills by:

- ***identifying pictures that are the same and pictures that are different;***
- ***finding smaller pictures within larger pictures;***
- ***telling a story based on pictures.***

Join the pictures that are the same.

Observe details

Ring the odd one out in each row.

Tell a story about the pictures.

10 Observe details

Ring the matching shadows.

Spot the differences in the pictures.

Observe details

Ring the things you can find in the big picture.

What can't you see in the picture?

Spot the differences in the pictures.

Observe details, tell a story

Finish the pictures on the right.

Tell a story about the pictures.

Observe details

Join the big shapes to the little shapes.

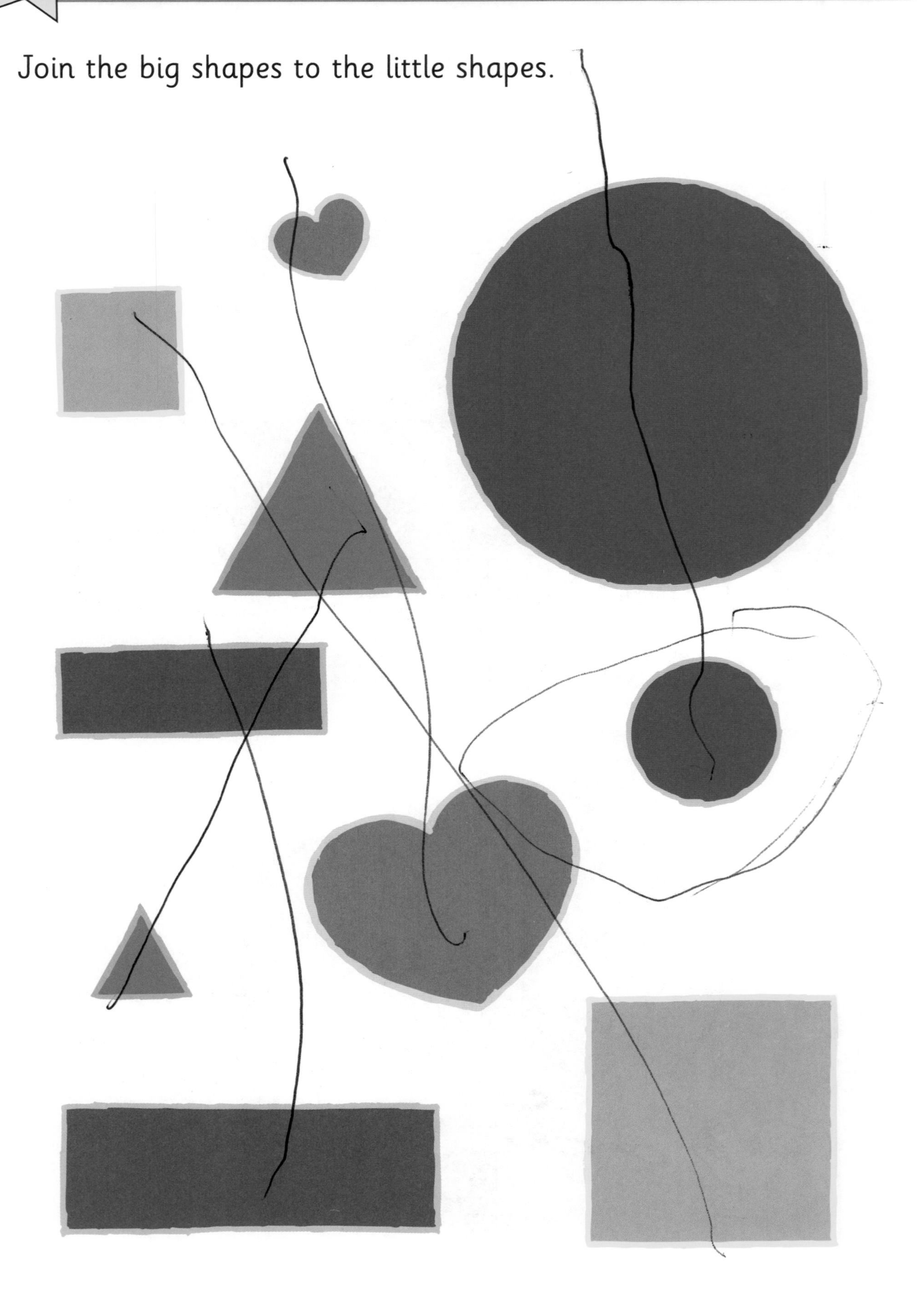

Join the things that go together.

18 How to say letter sounds

Words are made up of letters that have corresponding sounds. Children need to learn the sounds of the letters to help them read or 'decode' words. This is what teachers call 'phonics'.

The sound of the letter is not the same as its name; for example, the sound of b is 'buh' but its name is 'bee'.

Here are the single letter sounds you should start with. Pronounce the letter sounds as they appear in the examples below.

a as in apple (hard sound)
not as in angel (soft sound)
b as in bed
c as in cup
not as in circle
d as in dog
e as in egg
not as in eagle
f as in fish
g as in gate
not as in giraffe
h as in hen
i as in igloo or insect
not as in ice
j as in jug
k as in kite or kitten
l as in leaf
m as in moon or mum
n as in nest
o as in orange
not as in oval
p as in pen or penguin
q as in queen
r as in ring
s as in sun
t as in tap
u as in umbrella
not as in unicorn
v as in vase
w as in window
x as in box
not as in xylophone
y as in yellow or yo-yo
z as in zip or zebra

Later on, when your child is ready, you can point out that sometimes the same letter can have different sounds.

Do you know the sounds of all the letters?
Point to the sound that begins your name.

a b c d e

f g h i j k

l m n o p q

r s t u v w

x y z

Observe details

Ring the things that you can find in the big picture.

What can't you see in the picture?

Ring the odd one out in each row.

b d b b b b

c d c c c c

s s s s x s

a o o o o o

t f f f f f

Match pictures to sounds

Join the letters that are the same.

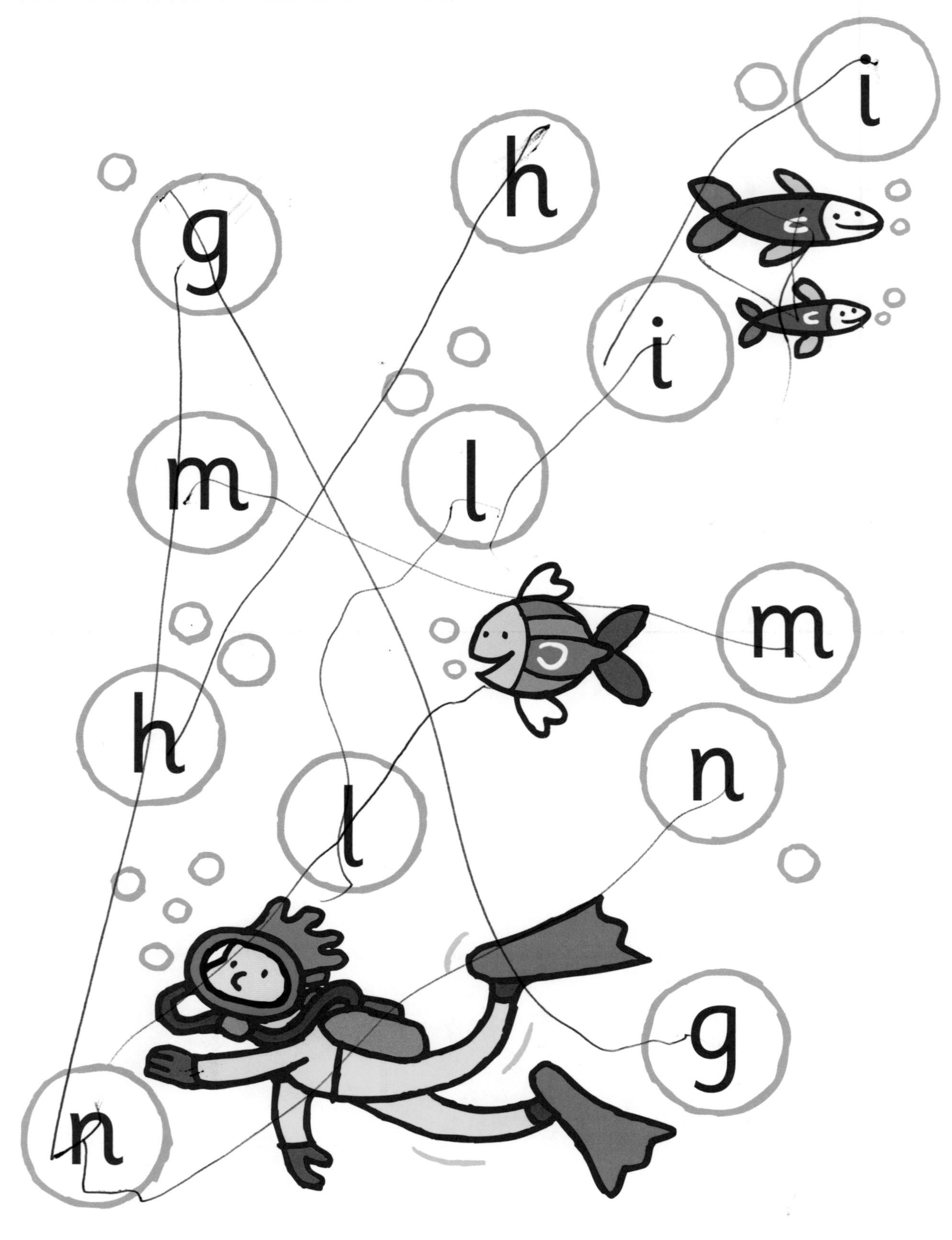

Match the pictures to the sounds.

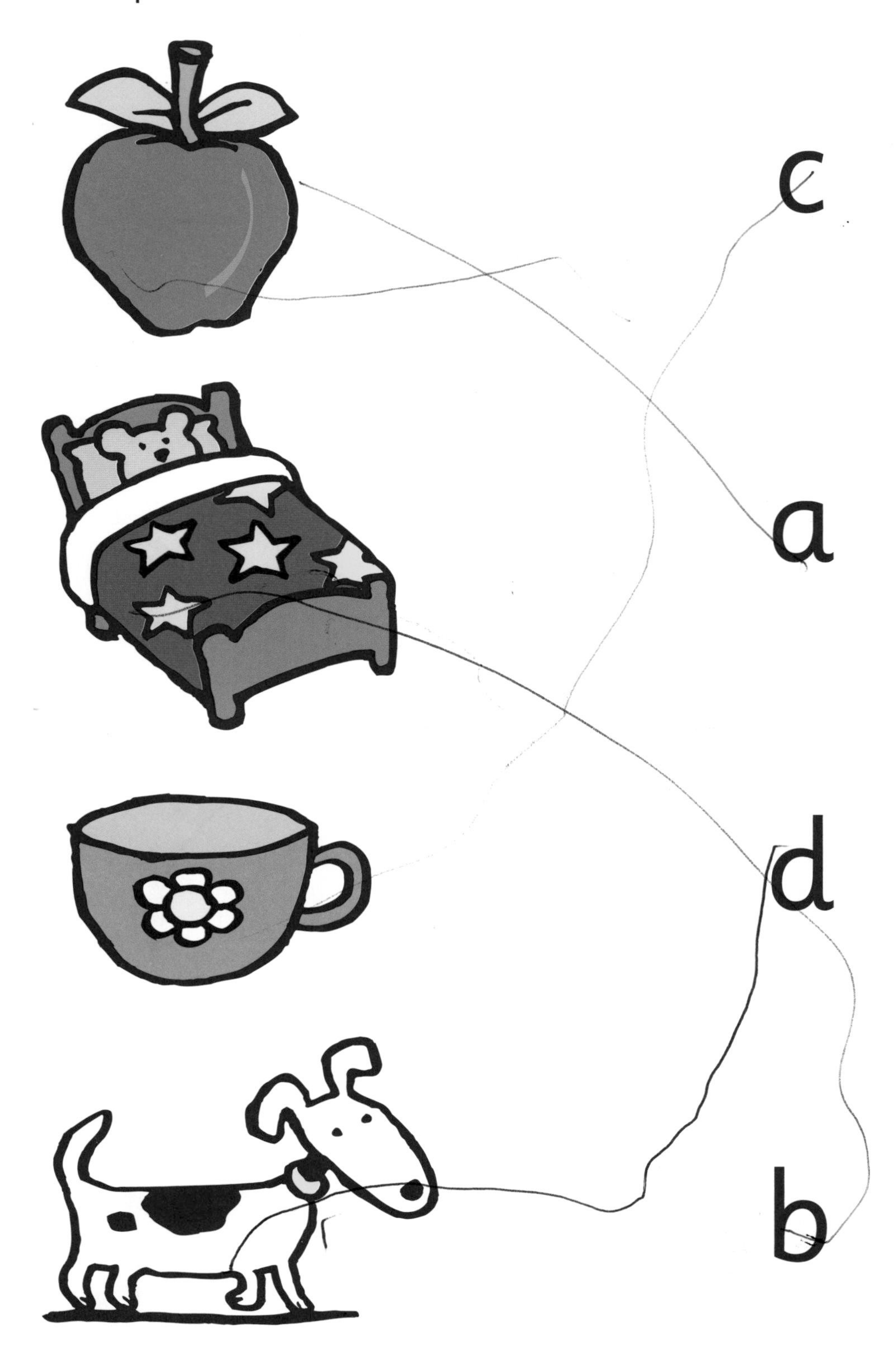

Match pictures to sounds

Match the pictures to the sounds.

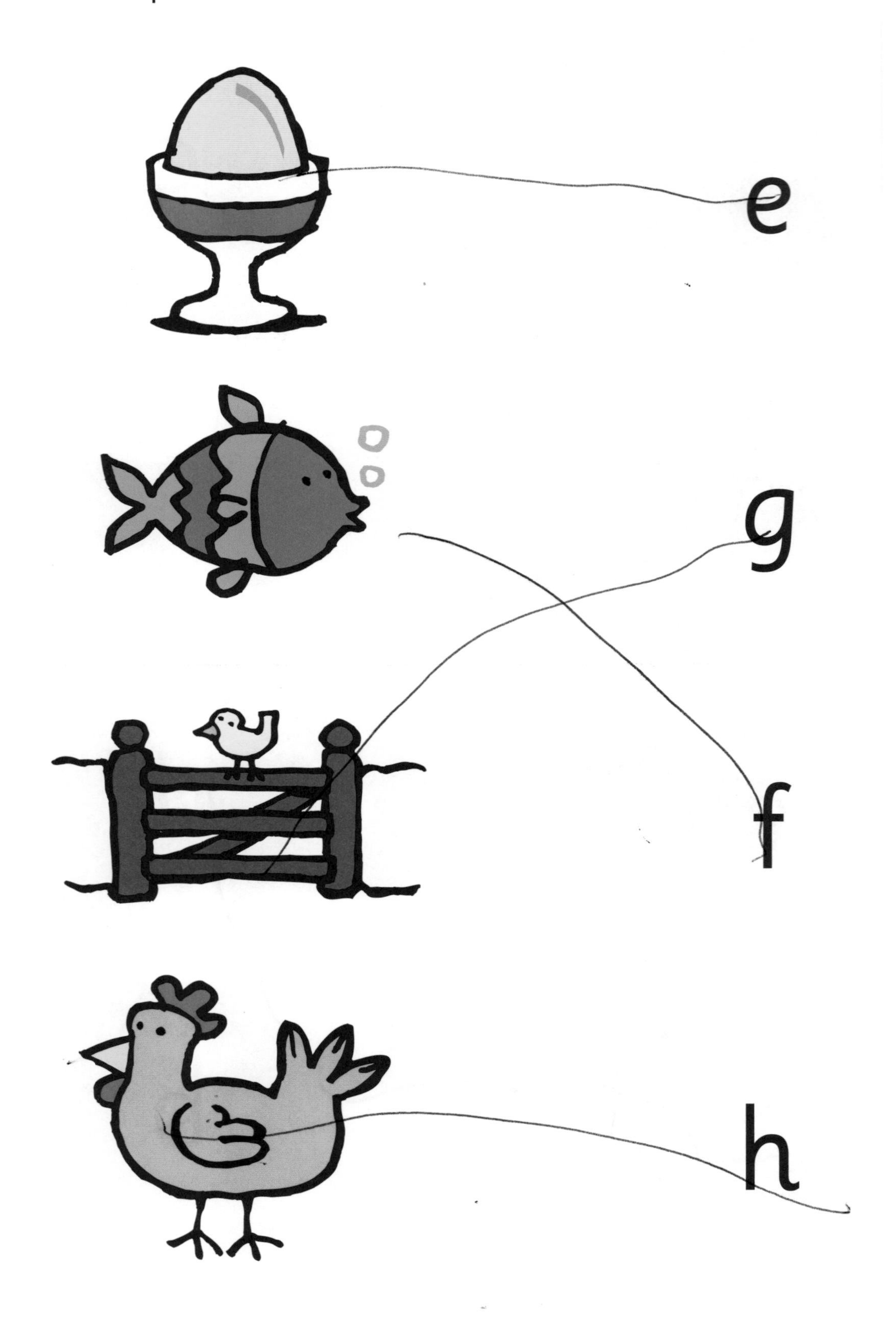

Match pictures to sounds

Match the pictures to the sounds.

26 Match pictures to sounds

Match the pictures to the sounds.

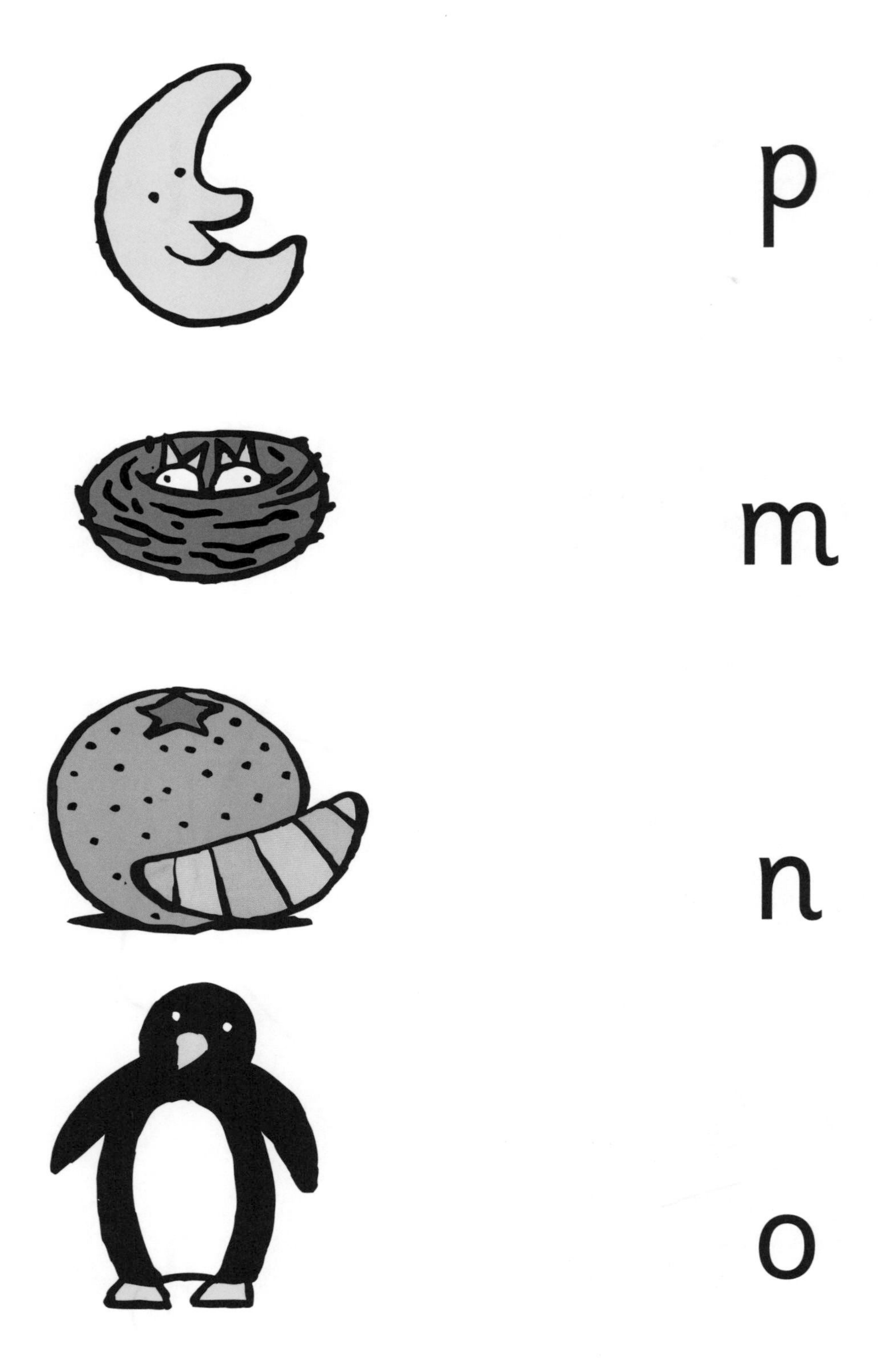

Match pictures to sounds

Match the pictures to the sounds.

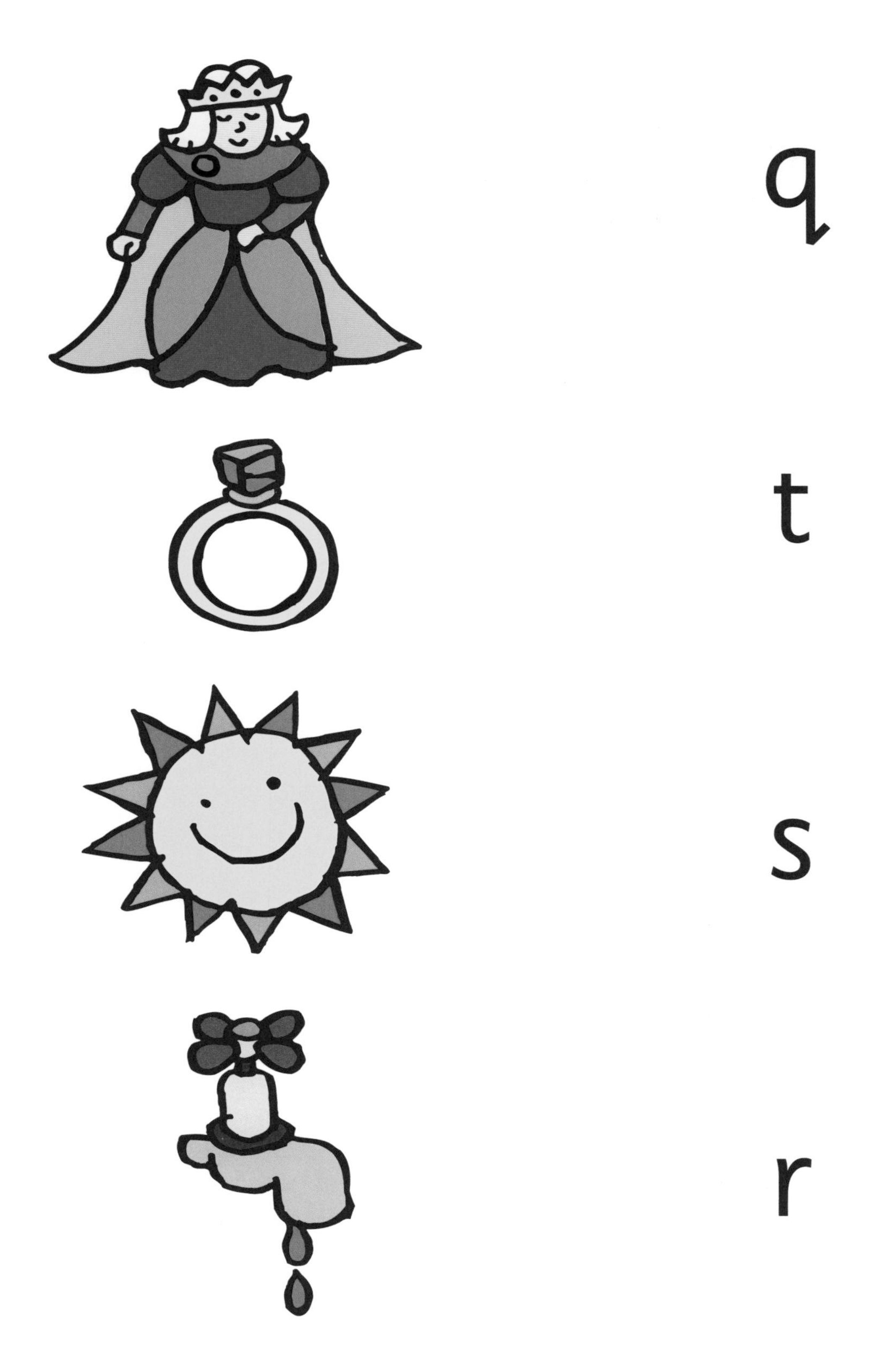

q

t

s

r

28 Match pictures to sounds

Match the pictures to the sounds.

u

Match the pictures to the sounds.

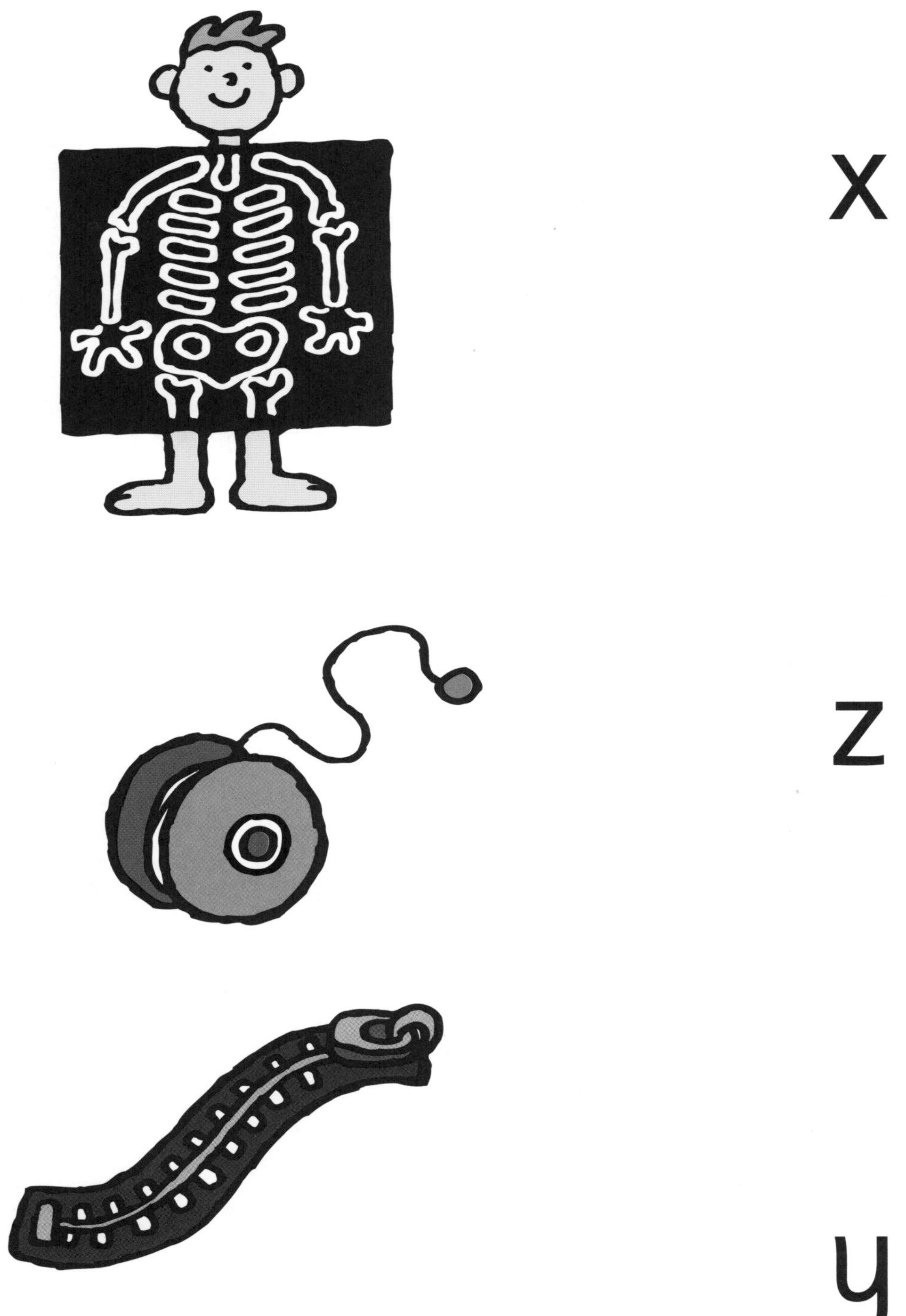

x

z

y

Tell a story, observe details

Tell a story about the pictures.

Ring the odd one out in each row.

j j j q j j

k k k k k z

p y p p p p

r r r r u r

w v v v v v

Match sounds to pictures

Ring the sounds that match the pictures.

e c

f h

t d

w s

Ring the sounds that match the pictures.

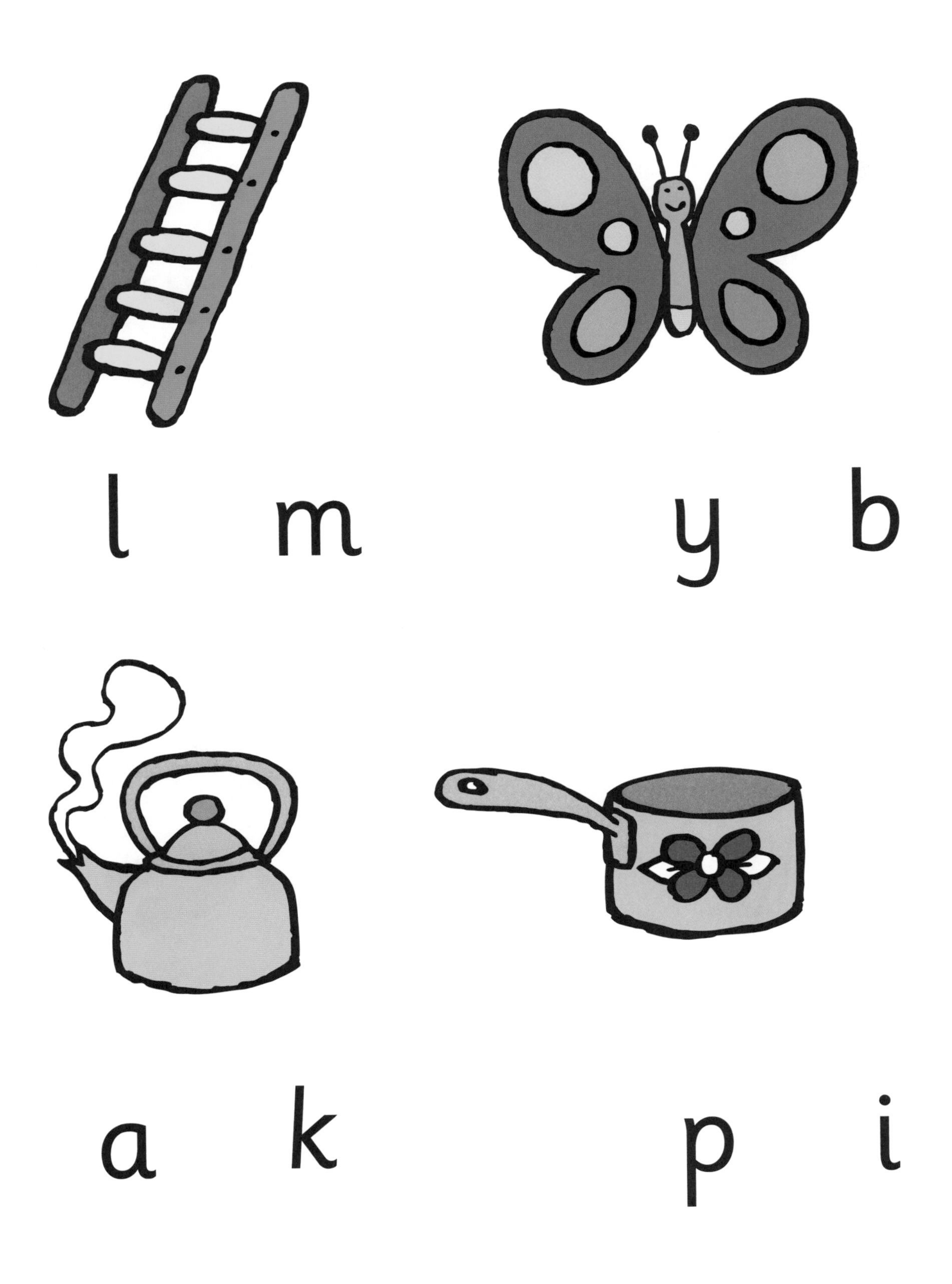

Match sounds to pictures, tell a story

Ring the sounds that match the pictures.

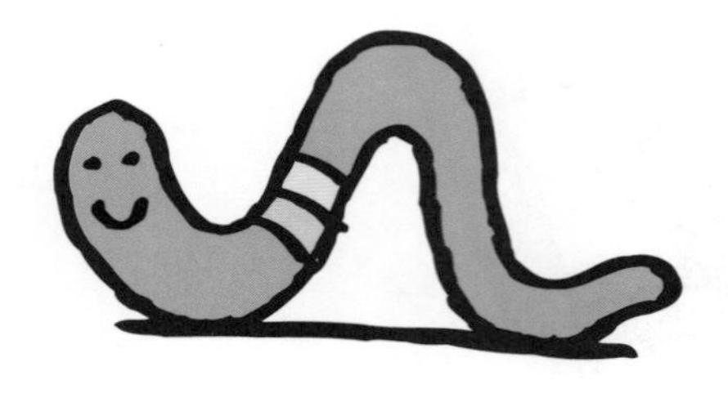

r q

w u

v z g

o x n

Tell a story about the pictures.

- **show your child your own writing, e.g. a list, or a message in a birthday card;**
- **encourage your child's 'pretend' writing;**
- **show your child that writing is fun.**

In this section we will be developing pencil control skills by:

- **drawing straight lines from left to right, and up and down;**
- **drawing circles in an anti-clockwise direction (in preparation for writing the letters o, a, e);**
- **drawing a variety of different lines, e.g. curved and zig-zag lines to encourage hand/eye co-ordination and fluent strokes.**

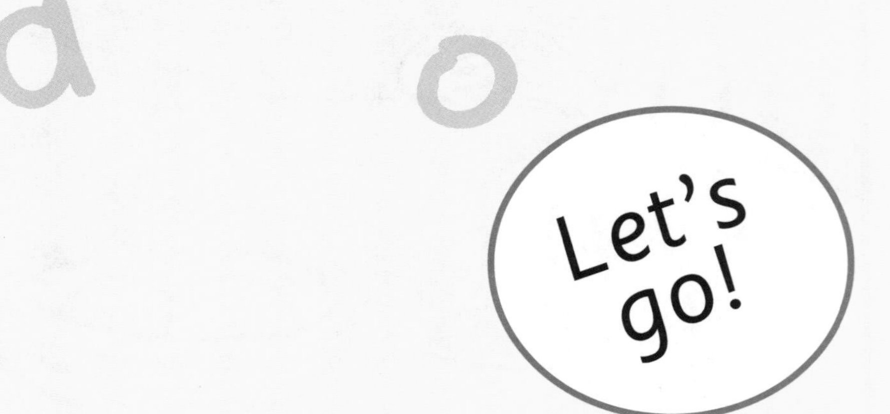

Draw the lines for the snails to follow.

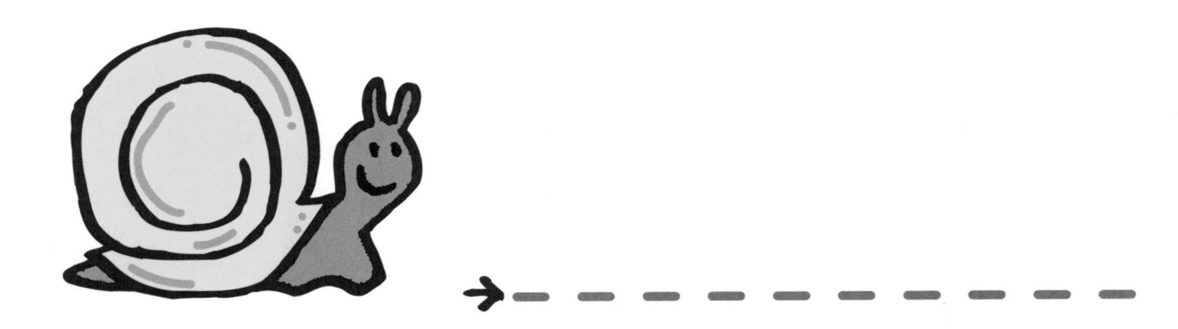

Draw left to right

Finish the ladders for the dogs to climb.

Show how the dolphins jump the waves.

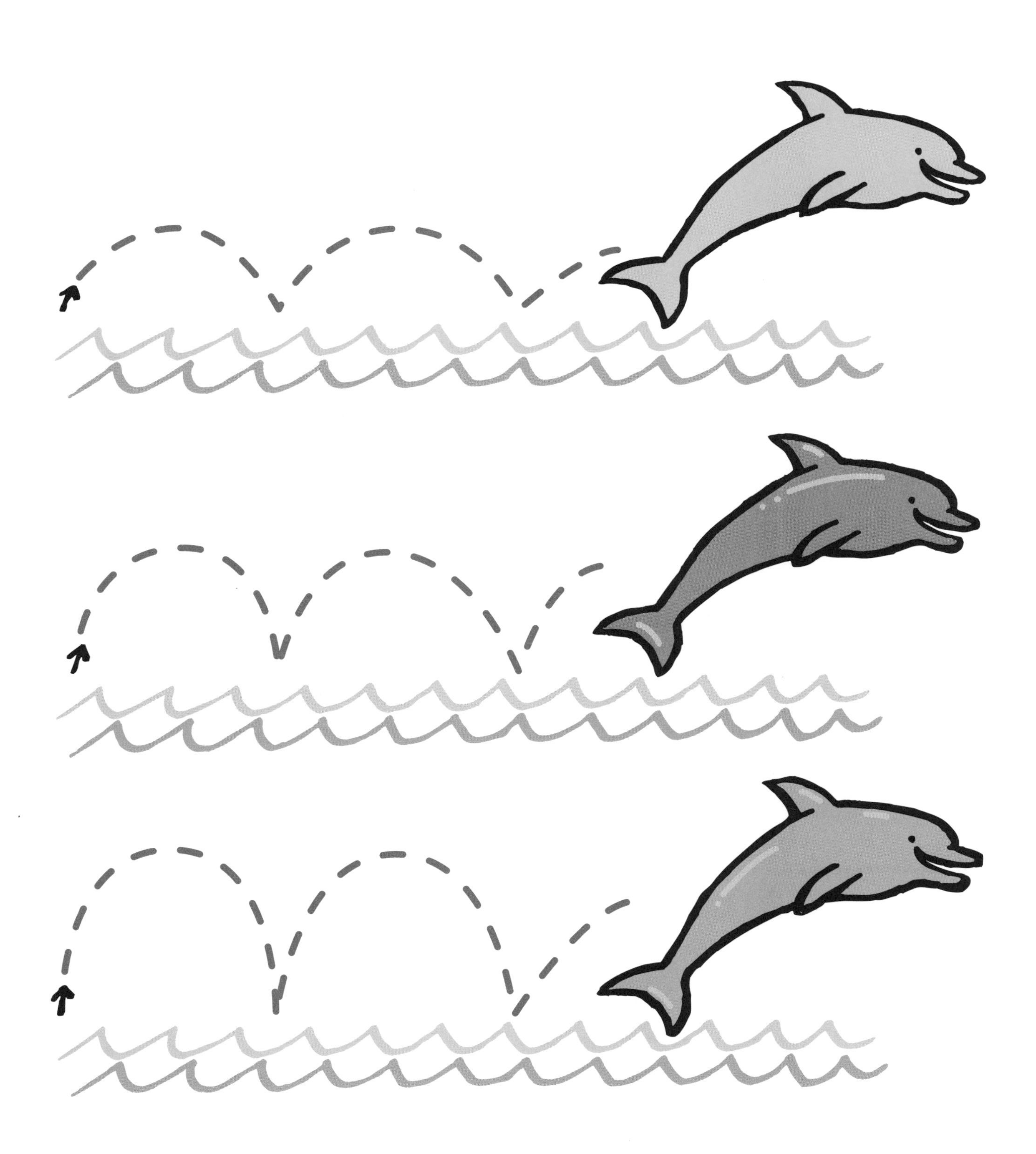

Draw straight and curved lines

Draw lines to finish the bricks on Humpty Dumpty's wall.

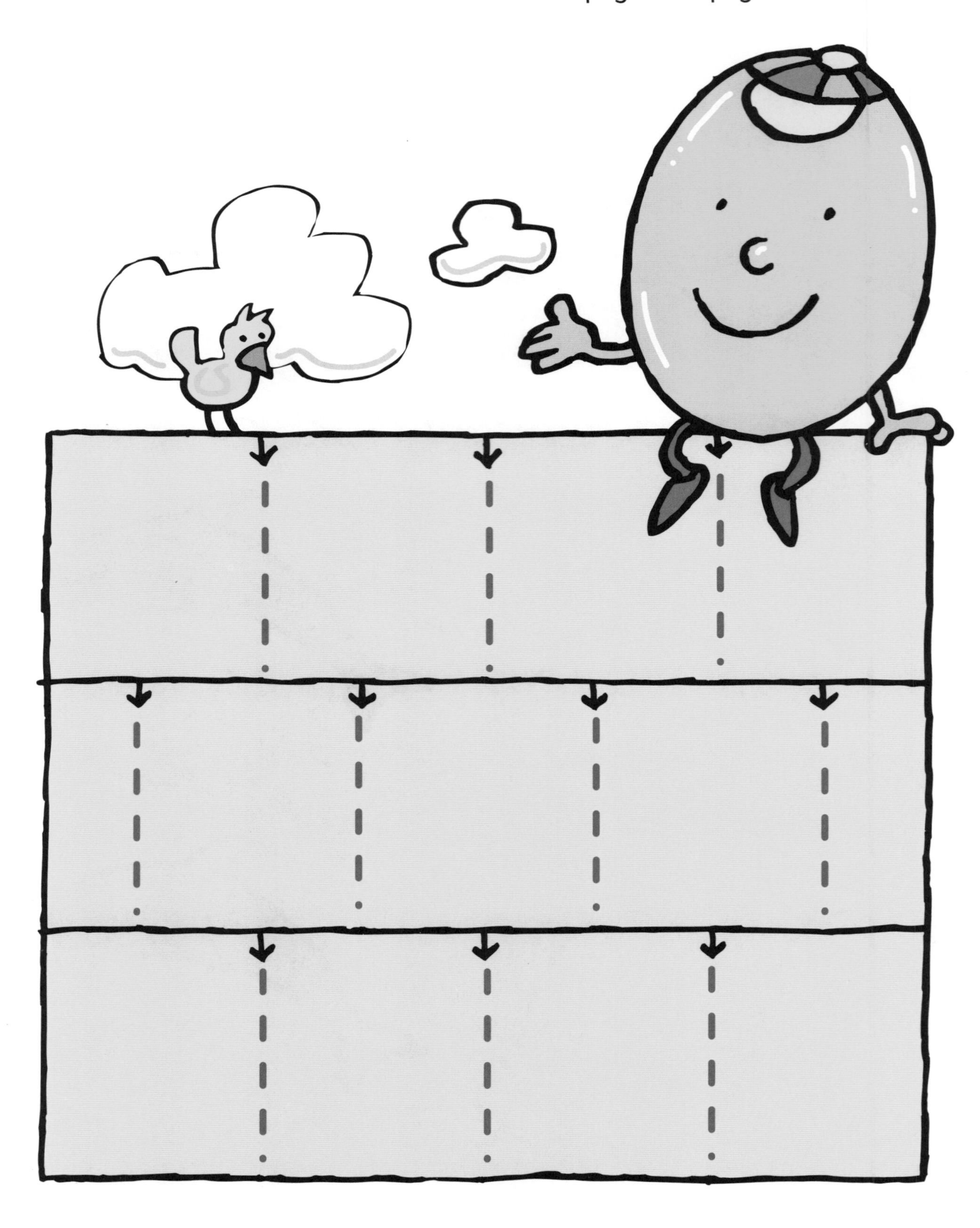

Show the mouse the way to his hole without touching the cat!

Draw straight and curved lines

Draw lines to finish the pattern on the rug.

Finish drawing the woolly lambs.

Draw circles

Draw drips of water falling from the watering can.

Draw a line to take the spaceship to the planet.

Draw lines in different directions

Show Jack and Jill the way up the hill.

Finish the pattern on the basket.

Draw lines in different directions

Show the tired teddy the way up the stairs.

Follow the lines to finish the weather house.

Draw diagonal and straight lines

Finish drawing the eggs.

Draw the legs on the little chicks.

Draw lines in different directions

Draw a towel for each teddy to lie on.

Draw the smiley sun in the sky.

Draw circles

Draw the wheels on the tractor.

Finish drawing the snowman and the snow penguin.

Draw diagonal and straight lines

Draw a climbing frame for the monkeys.

Draw a swing and a slide for the rabbits.

Draw curved lines

Give the little babies lots of curls.

Draw patterns on the slithery snakes.

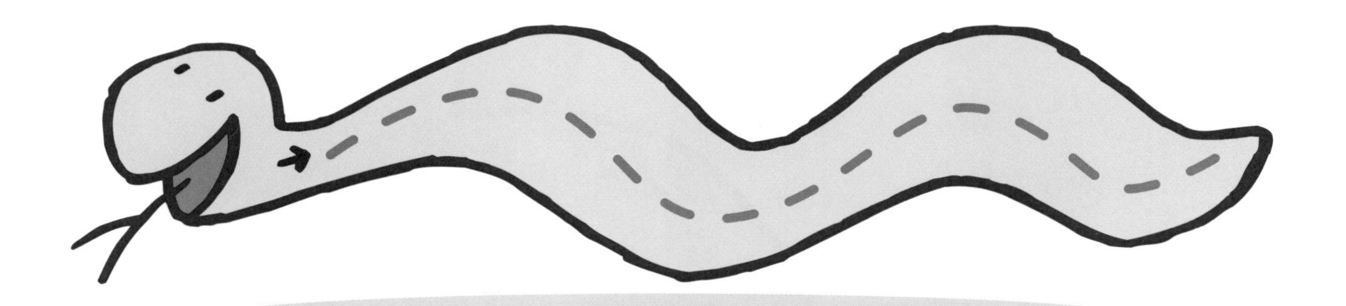

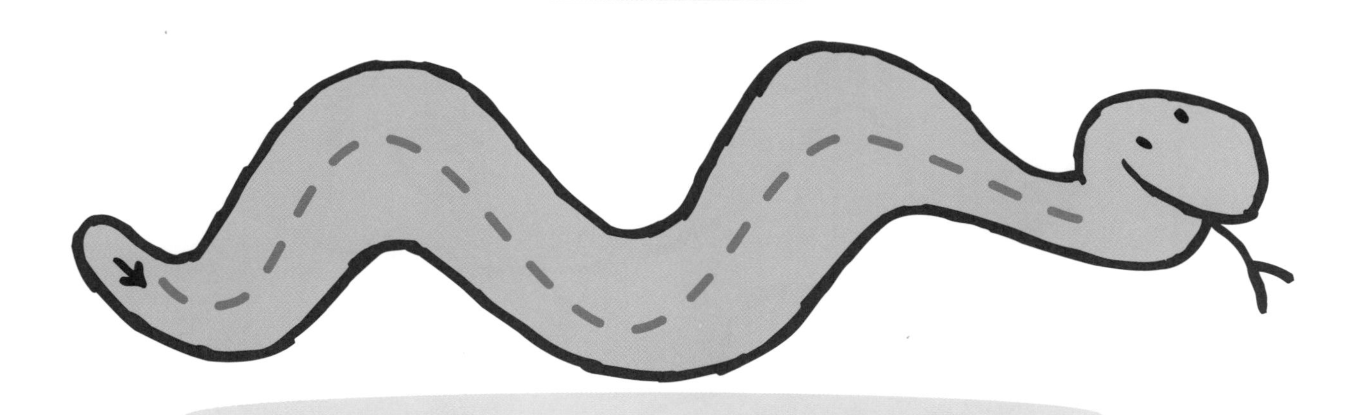

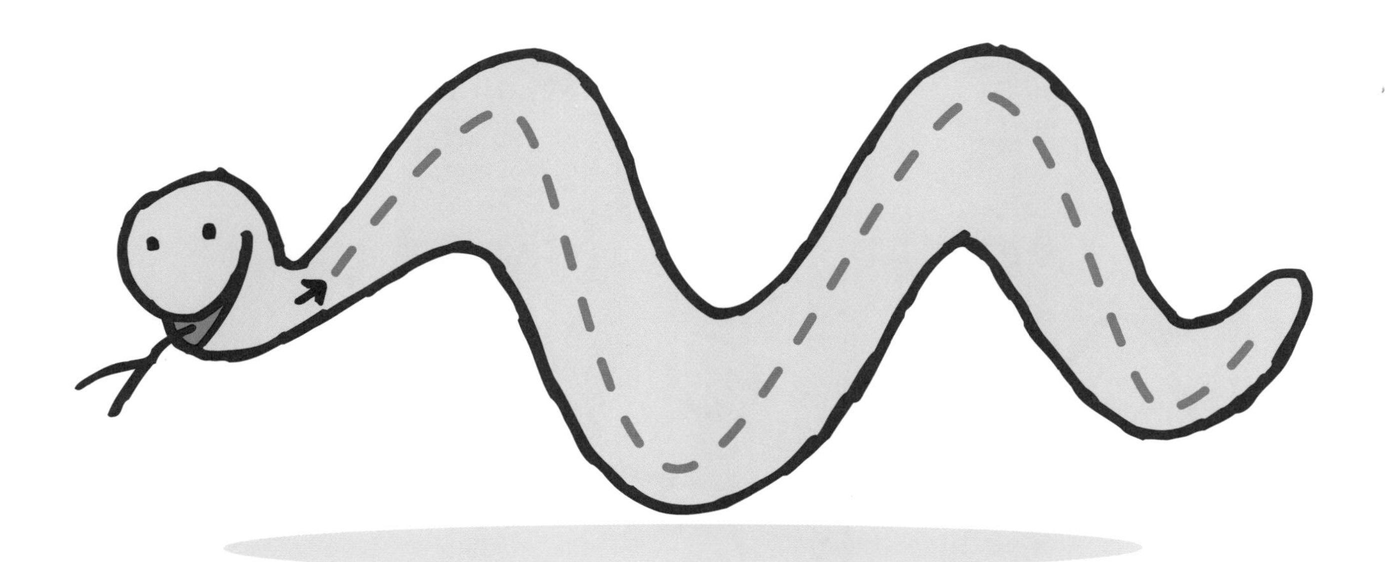

Draw curved lines

Draw the scales on the bottom fish to make him look like his friend.

Draw some waves for the whale to swim in.

Draw a variety of lines

Finish drawing the castle.

Draw the pattern on the knitting.

How to read words

To be able to read a particular word, your child needs to identify the different sounds in that word.

Encourage your child to:

- **point to the first letter in the word;**
- **sound out the letter;**
- **point to the next letter(s);**
- **sound out the letter(s);**
- **then 'blend' the sounds together to say the word.**

Don't let your child struggle too long with a word; quickly offer help rather than 'waiting' for a reply. Don't hide the pictures – these are visual clues.

Some words can't be read phonetically and are best learnt as a whole word, for example: the, where, was.
We learn to read these words by familiarity and remembering them as a whole shape.

Look at each picture and say the word.

apple

bed

cup

dog

Recognise sounds in words

Look at each picture and say the word.

egg

fish

In **gate**, the **e** softens the sound of the letter **a**.

fish has three sounds, not four.

gate

horse

Look at each picture and say the word.

insect

jelly

key

log

Recognise sounds in words

Look at each picture and say the word.

moon

nest

orange

penguin

Look at each picture and say the word.

queen

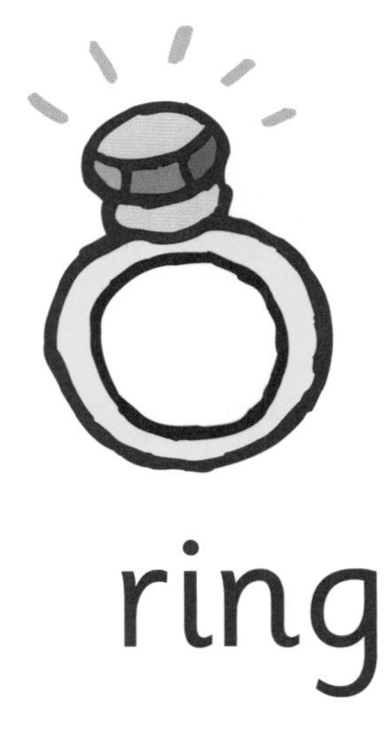

ring

In **table**, the **e** softens the sound of the letter **a**.

sun

table

Recognise sounds in words

Look at each picture and say the word.

umbrella

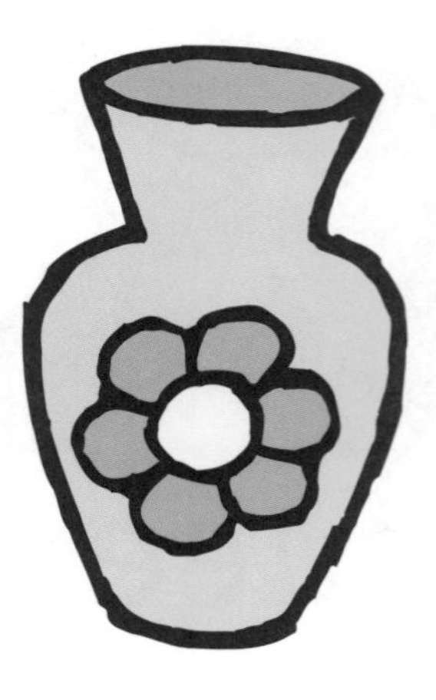

vase

window

Look at each picture and say the word.

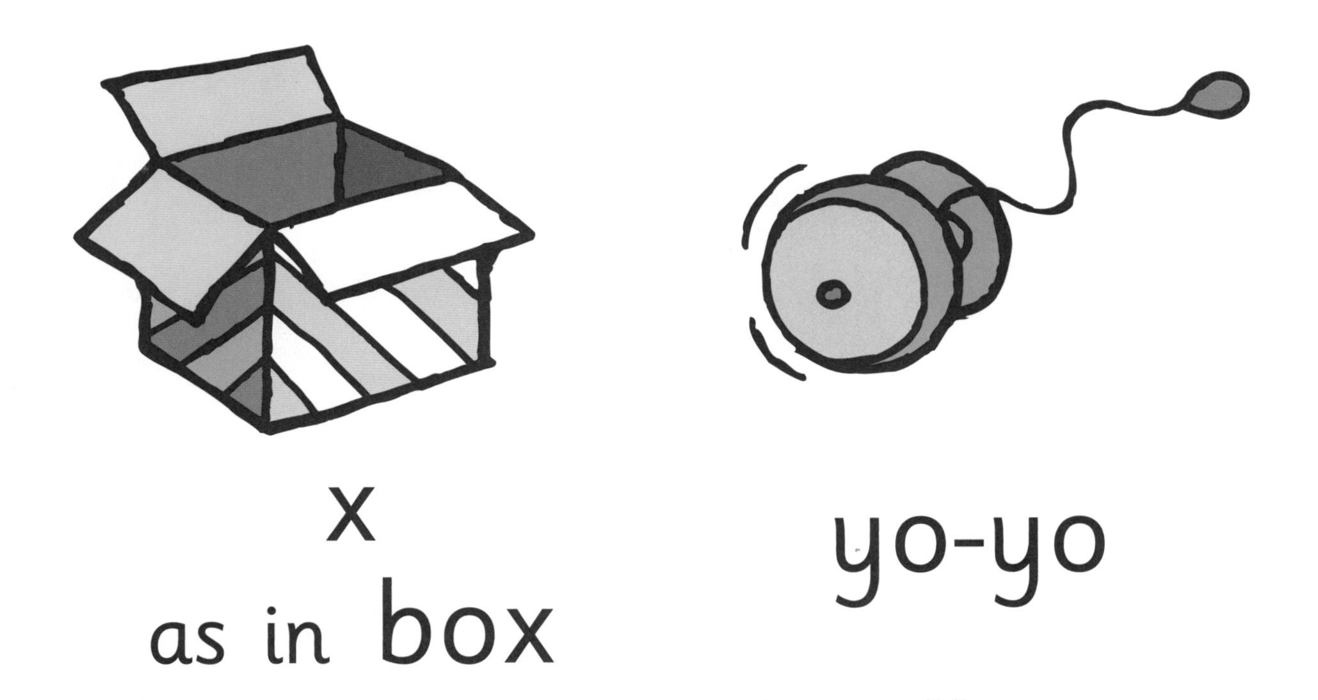

x
as in box

yo-yo

zebra

Tell a story, say letter sounds

Tell a story about the pictures.

One hot day ...

Match the letters to the pictures.

a f k s

Say letter sounds

Say the sounds.
Ring the pictures that match the sounds.

d		
m		
p		
t		

Colour the picture using the key.

b is for blue.

r is for red.

g is for green.

y is for yellow.

Say and read words

Colour the pictures.

blue car

green frog

red ball

yellow sun

Ring the same words in each row.

 **gate**	jam	gate	pin
 **horse**	horse	dog	cat
 **insect**	leg	apple	insect
 **jam**	gate	pan	jam

Match pictures and words

Ring the words that match the pictures.

pen / king

log / cat

moon / cow

nest / bag

Ring the words that match the pictures.

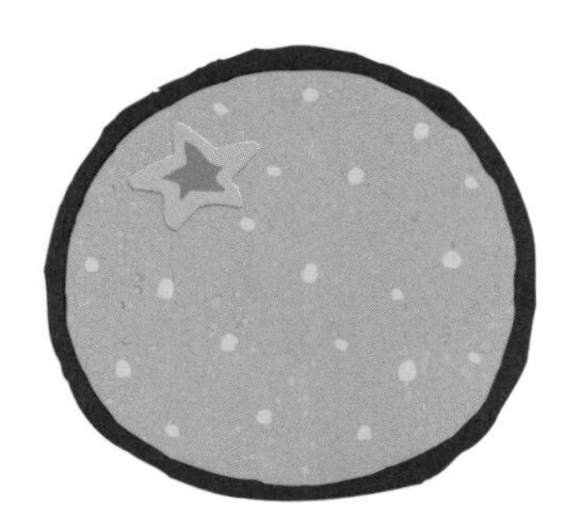

orange
one

pin
pan

queen
quilt

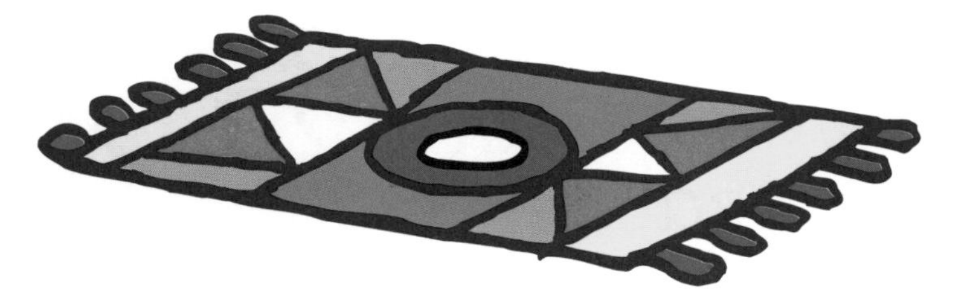

red
rug

Say letter sounds

Colour the things in the picture that begin with s.

Colour the things in the picture that begin with t.

Say and read words

Look at the pictures. Read the words.
Draw the pictures in the boxes.

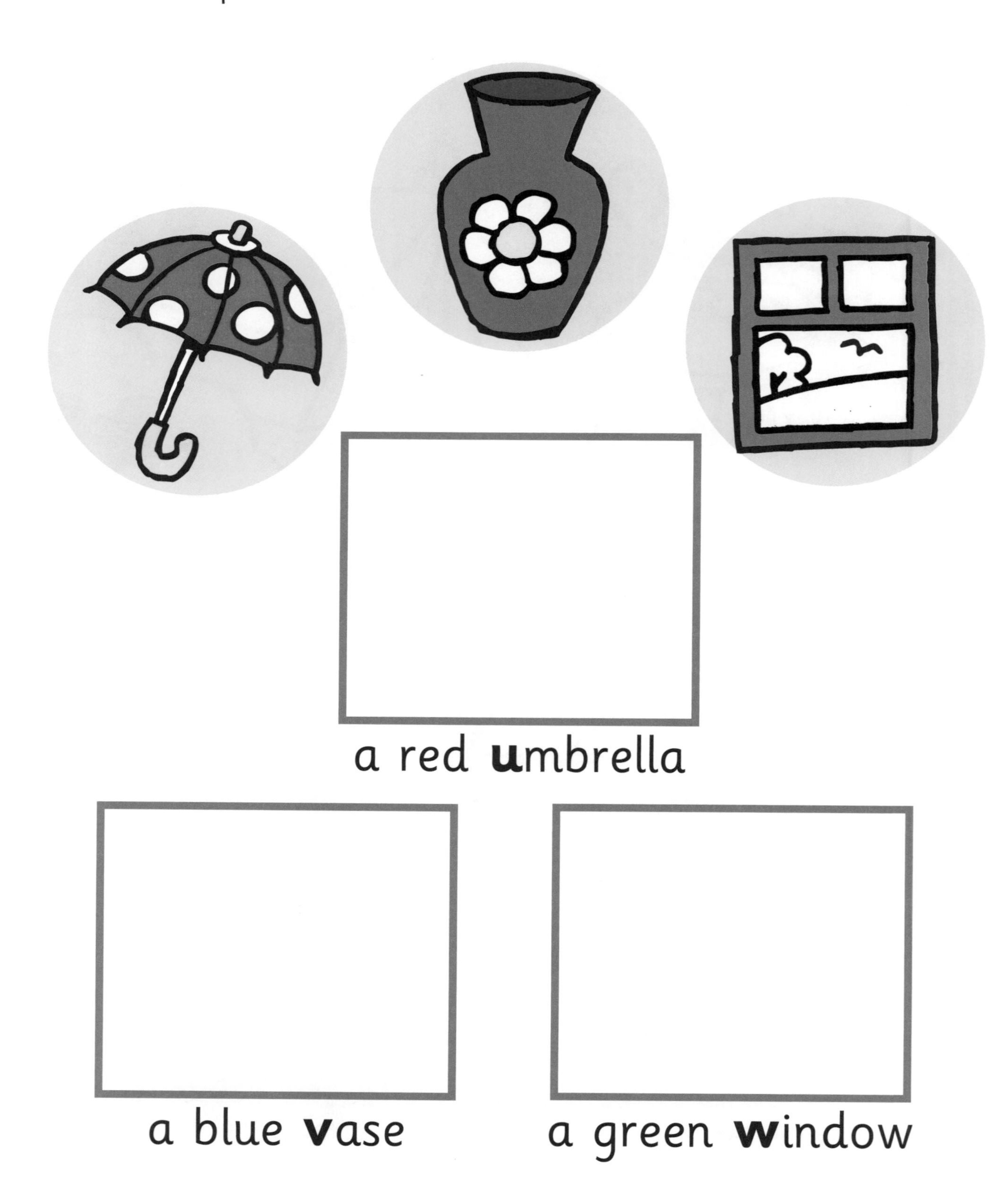

Look at the pictures. Read the words.
Draw the pictures in the boxes.

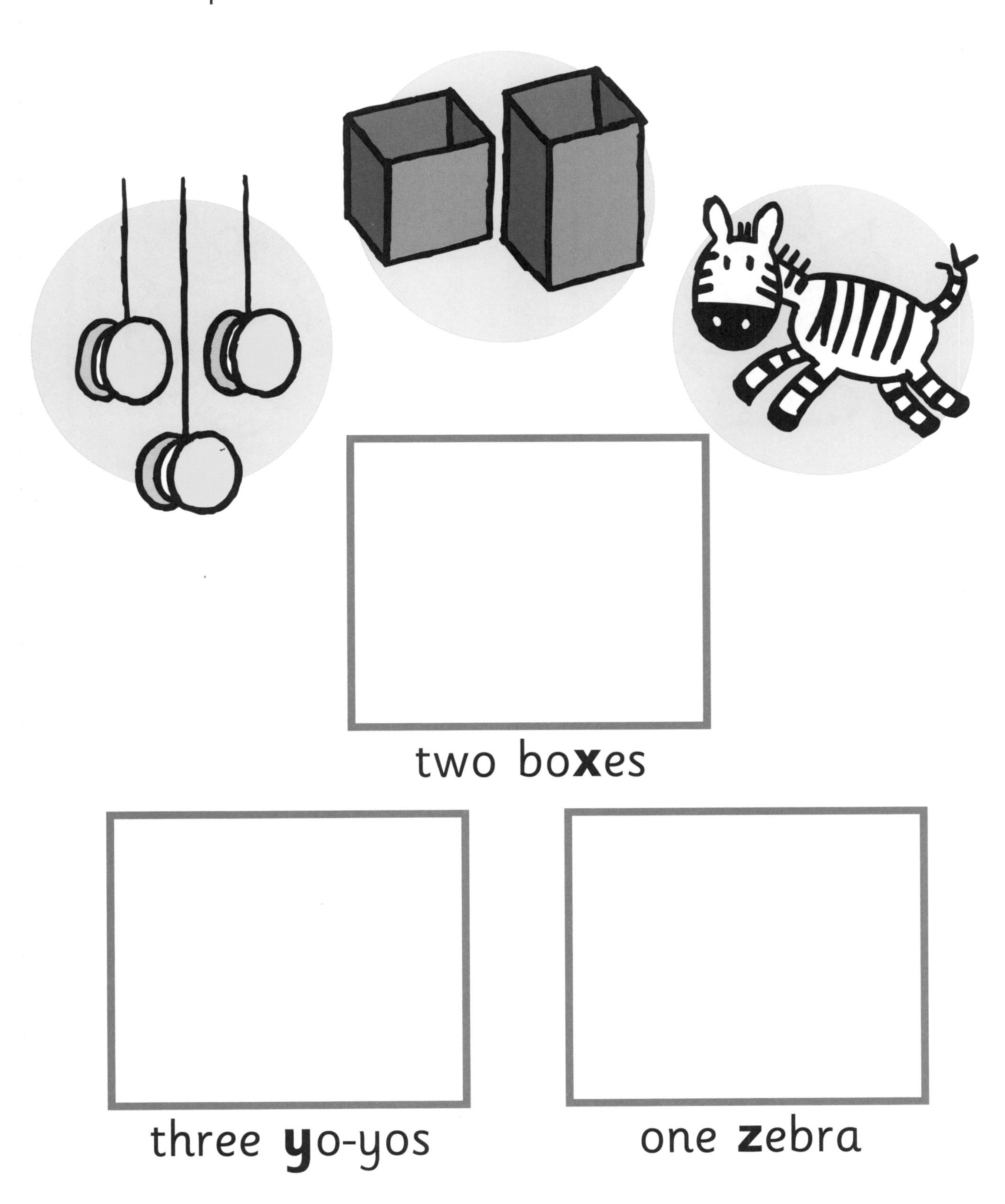

What do you like best of all?

I like to ...

read

play

dance

draw

Tell a story about the pictures.

One windy day ...

Say and read words

Look at the pictures. Read the words.
Copy the pictures into the boxes.

a dog

a cat

Can you read the words?

A dog and a cat can ...

run

jump

eat

sleep

Read words, say a rhyme

Read the words.

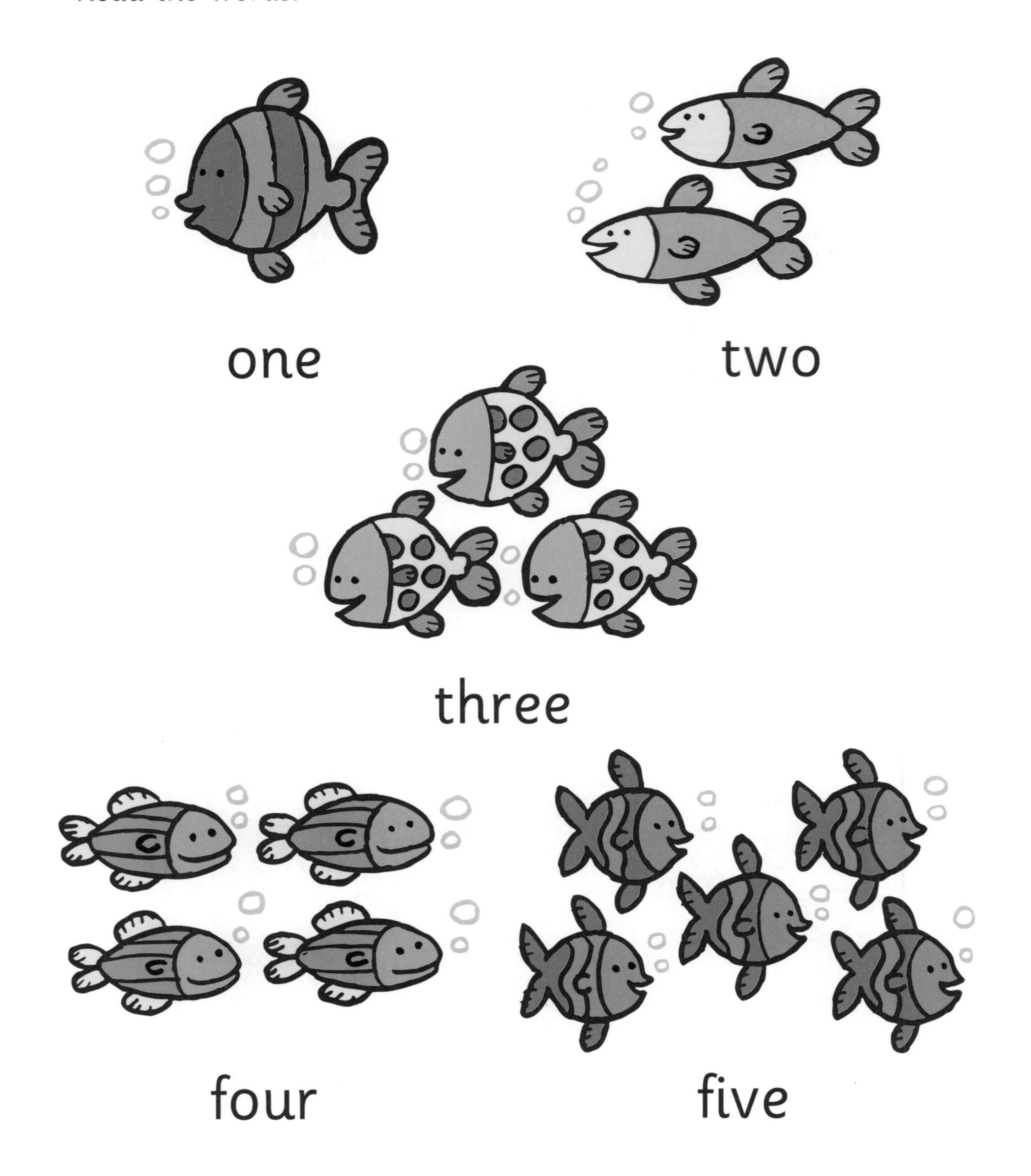

Say the rhyme.

one two
three four five

once I caught a fish alive

six seven
eight nine ten

then I let it go again!

Observe details

Tick the picture that comes first.

Tick the picture that comes first.

Join the words that are the same.

mum dad boy girl baby

Observe details, read words

Ring the odd one out in each row.

the	the	he	the
in	on	in	in
and	a	and	and
is	it	it	it
dad	dad	dad	day

Read the words.
Draw a picture for each animal.

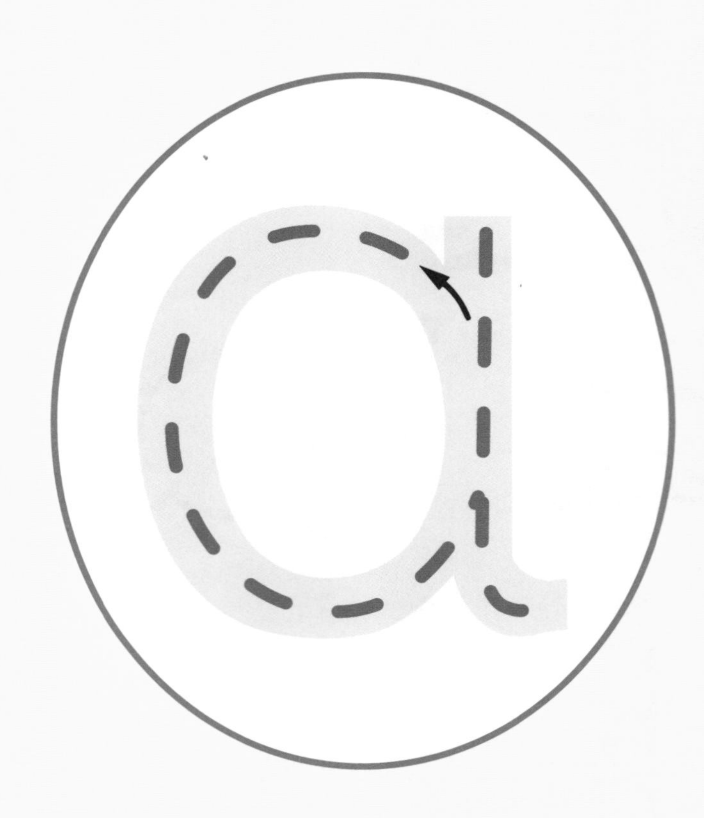

The next pages will show you how to write each letter of the alphabet.
Start at the black arrow and follow the blue dashes. Try to keep inside the blue shadow.

a a a a a a

There are several chances to write each letter because **practice makes perfect!**

It is important that children learn to form the letters correctly, but do remember that writing is a difficult skill for children of this age and you shouldn't worry too much about neatness and correctness at the beginning.

With younger children, you could practise writing letters in a sand tray or "sky writing" (writing letters in the air with a pointed finger).

Children who are left-handed sometimes write letters in a different direction from the ways shown here and this is not a problem as long as their own style is legible and efficient.

Sit at a table to do your best writing!

Write a and b

Follow the ant on the apple to write **a**.

Write **a** on the line.

a

Write **b** on the balloons.

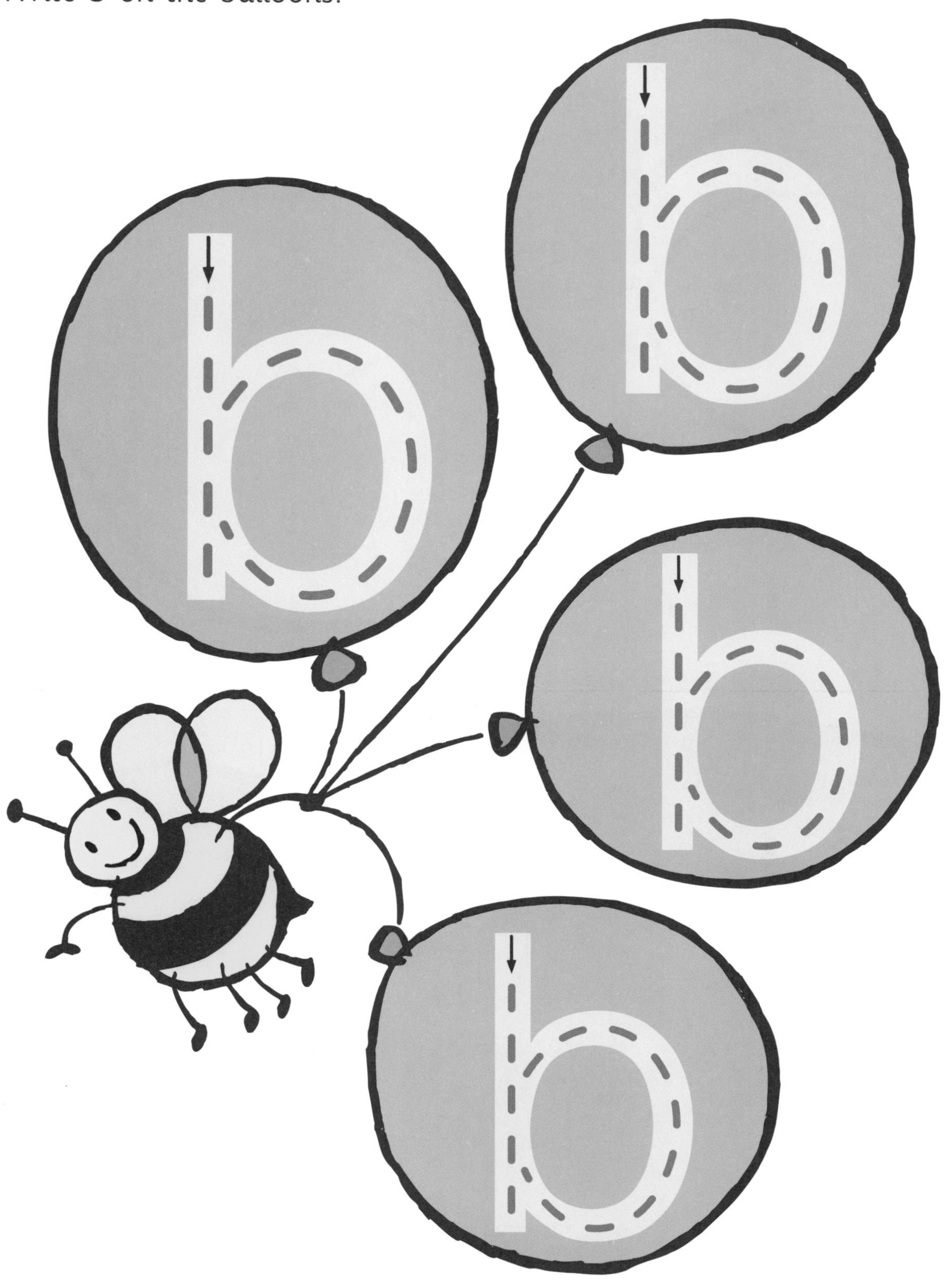

Write c and d

Finish the **c** pattern on the cups.

Write **d** to finish the dog.

Write **d** on the line.

d

100 Write e and f

Write **e** on the egg cups.

Write **f** to finish the fence.

Write **f** on the line.

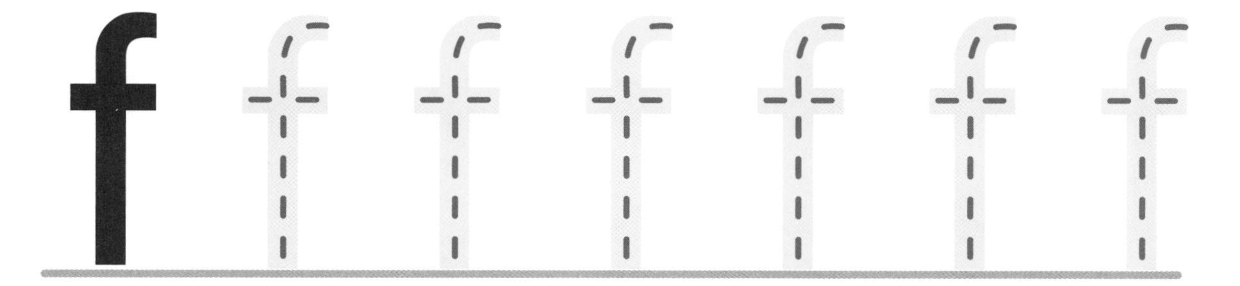

Write g and h

Write **g** to take the goat through the garden.

Write **g** on the line.

g g g g g g

Write **h** to march the men down the hill.

Write **h** on the line.

Write i and j

Write **i** to put the icing on the cake.

Write **j** to finish the pattern on the jacket.

Write k and l

Write **k** on the kites.

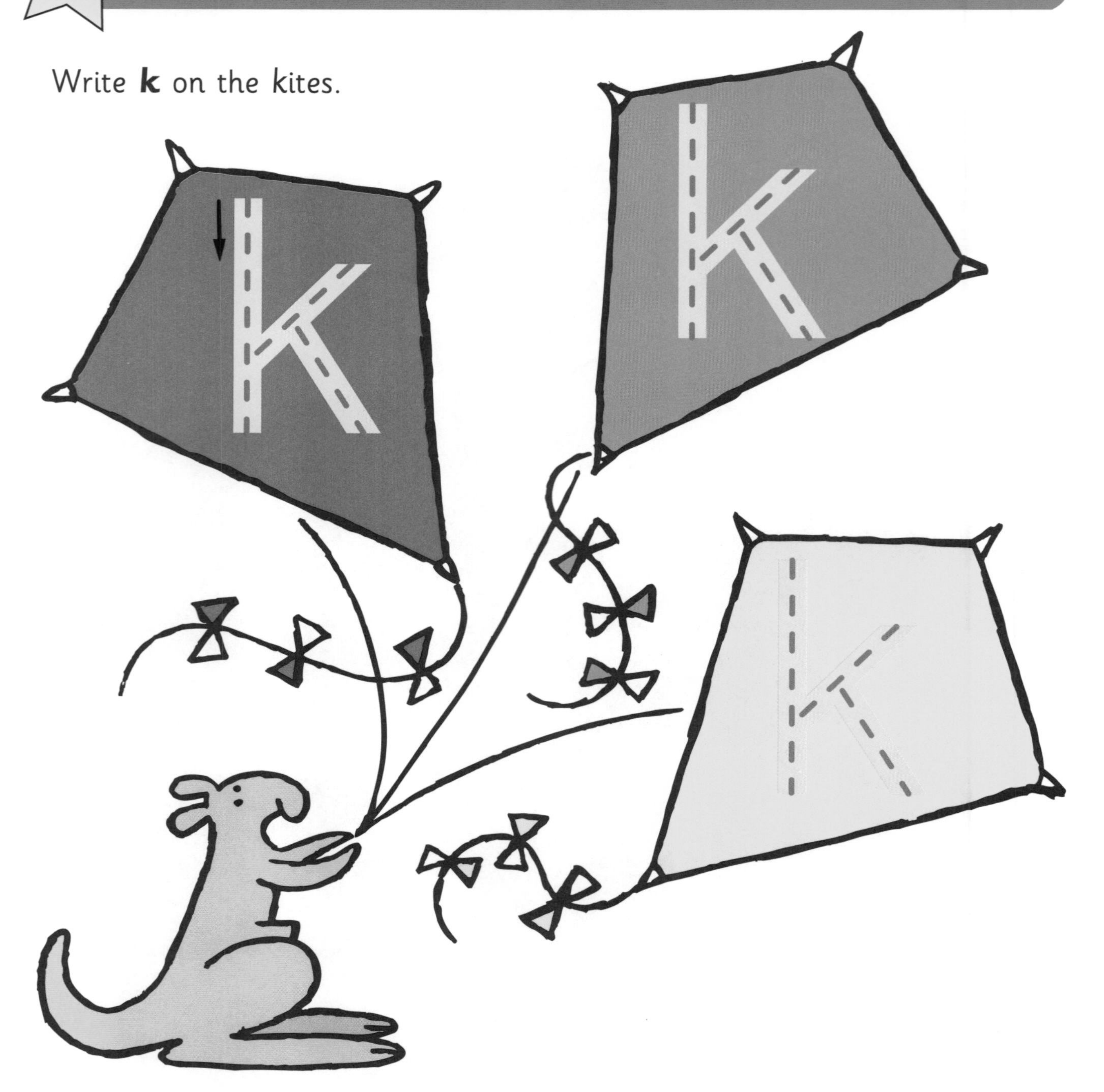

Write **k** on the line.

Write **l** to finish the lorry.

Write **l** on the line.

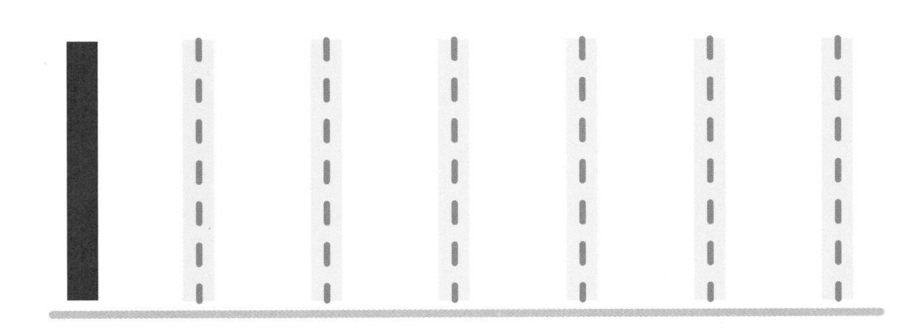

Write m and n

Write **m** to show the mouse the way to the cheese.

Write **m** on the line.

Write **n** on the beads on Ted's necklace.

Write o and p

Write **o** on the oranges.

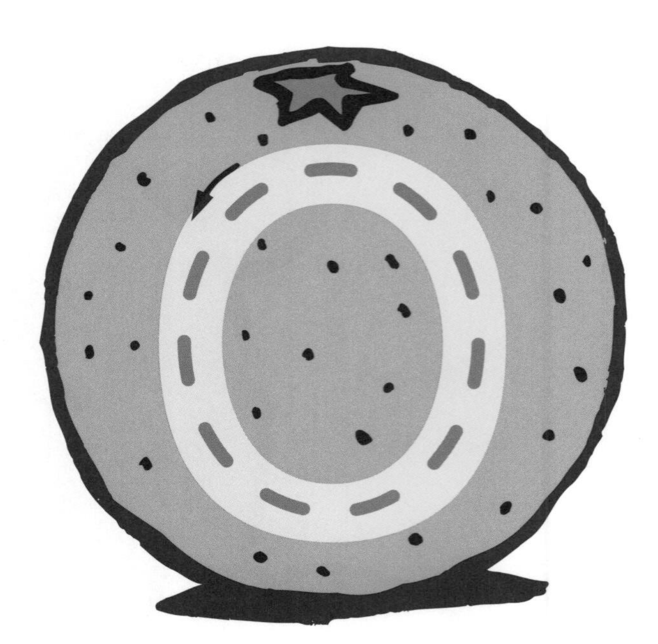

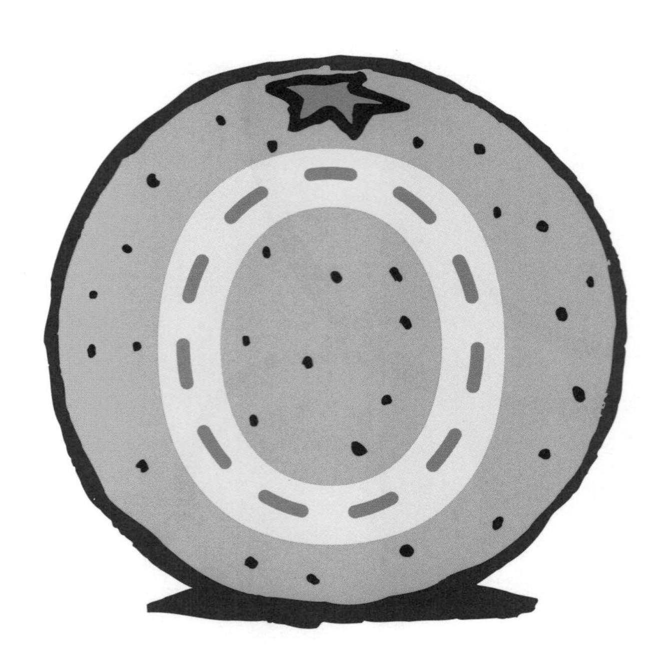

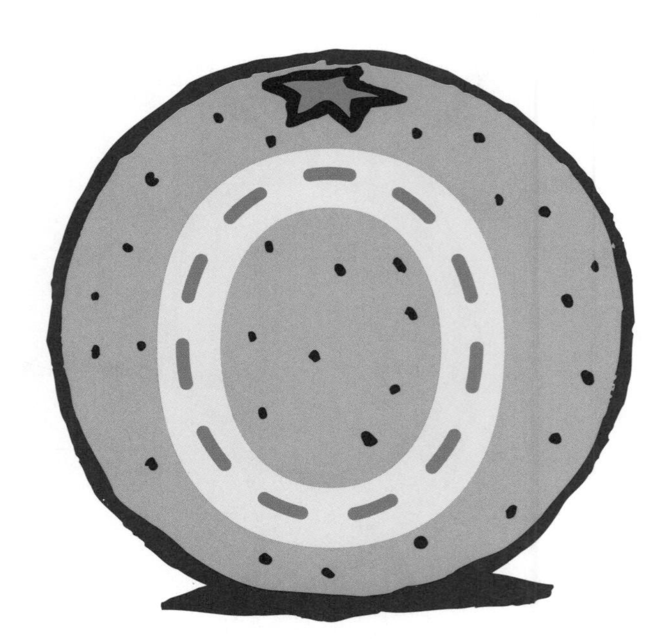

Write **o** on the line.

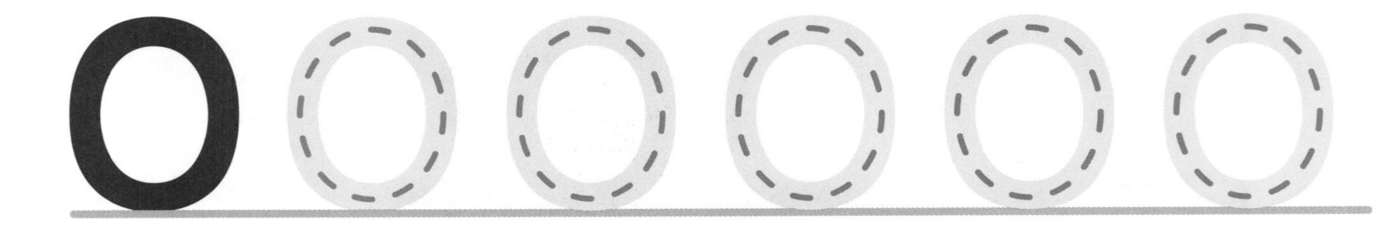

Write o and p

Write **p** on the peacock.

Write q and r

Write **q** on the pieces of the patchwork quilt.

Write **r** on the rattlesnake to finish the pattern on his skin.

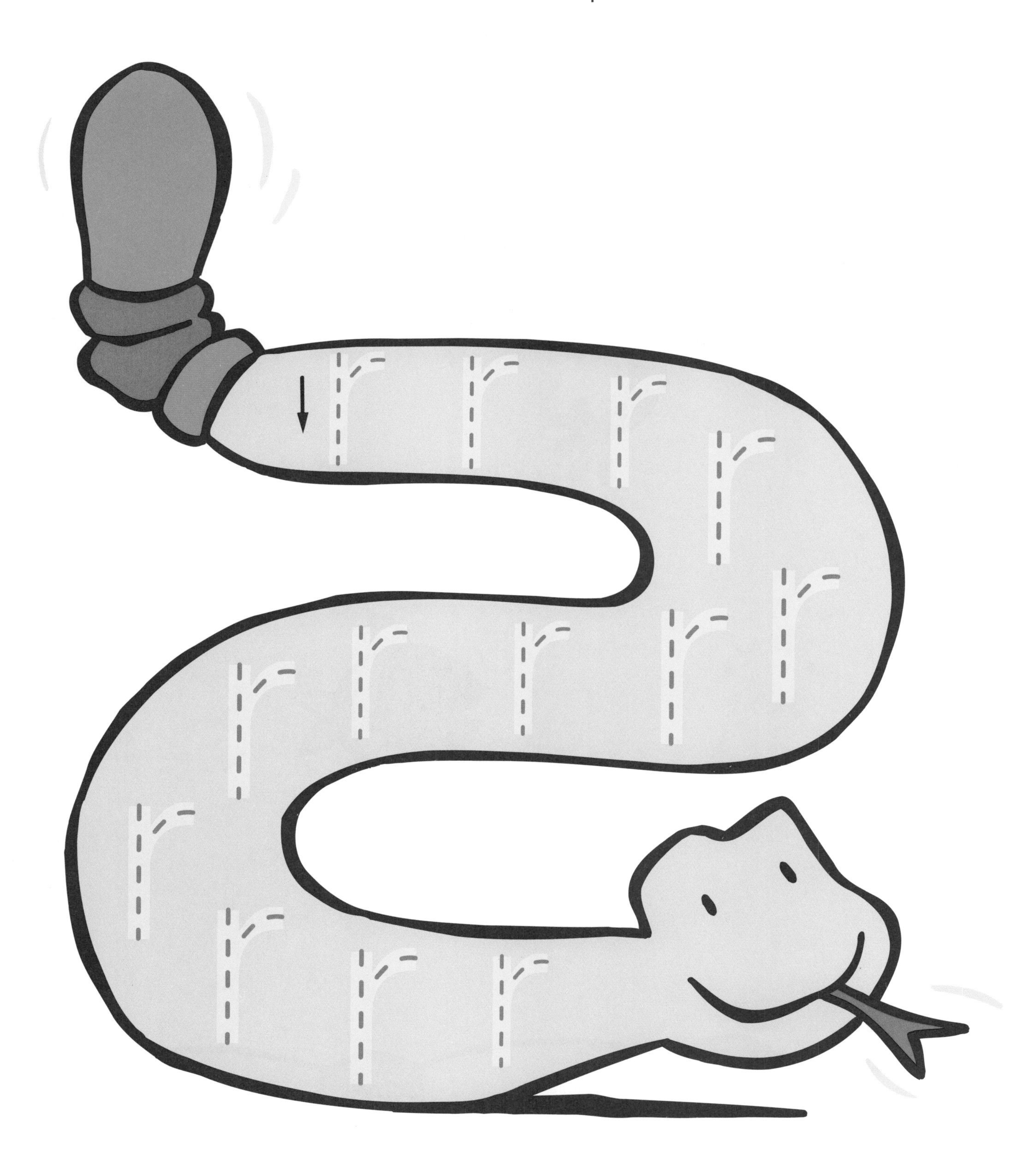

Write s and t

Write **s** to finish the seaweed.

Write **t** on the tortoises.

Write **t** on the line.

Write u and v

Write **u** on the umbrella.

Write **v** to finish the pattern on the vase.

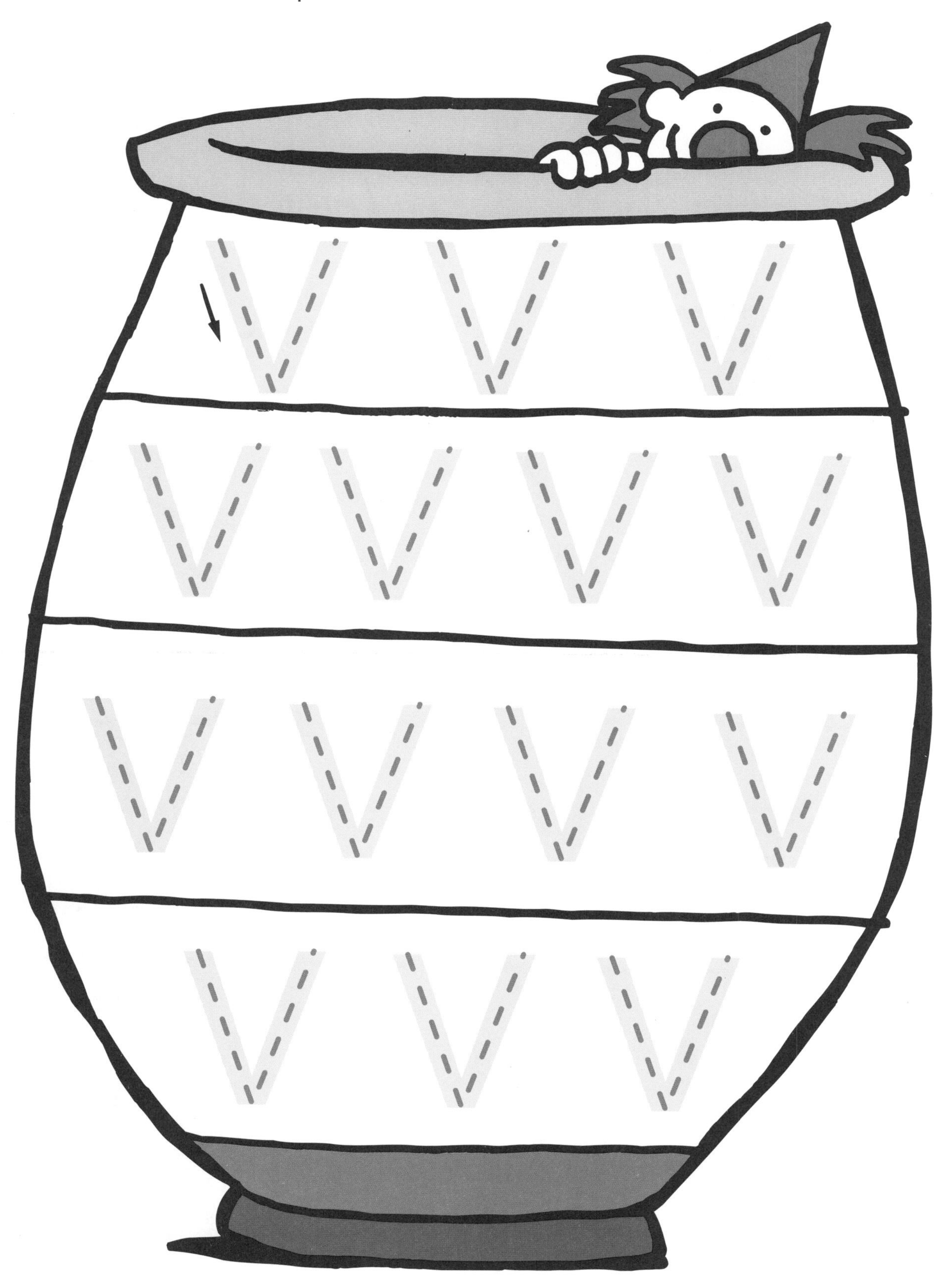

Write w and x

Write **w** on the bricks in the wall.

Write **x** on the card tied to the gift box.

Write **x** on the line.

Write y and z

Write **y** on the yo-yos.

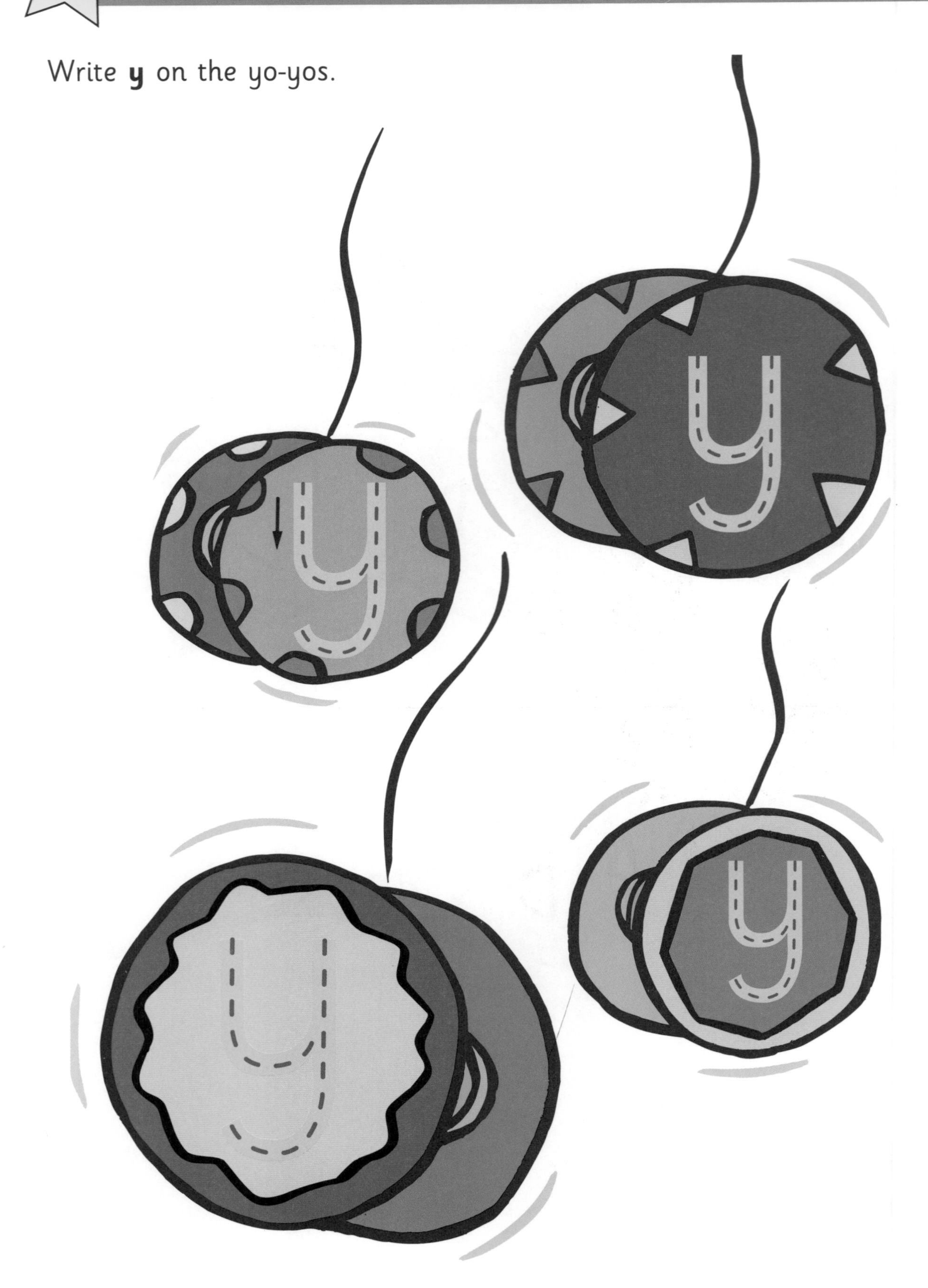

Write **z** to finish the sleepy zebra's coat.

Write **z** on the line.

z

Match letter shapes

The clown is juggling letters.
Write the letters in the matching shapes.

Write your name

Ask a grown-up to write your name on the line below.

Well done, ________________________ .

Now you can practise writing your name on these lines.

Write the alphabet

Write the alphabet on the centipede's body.

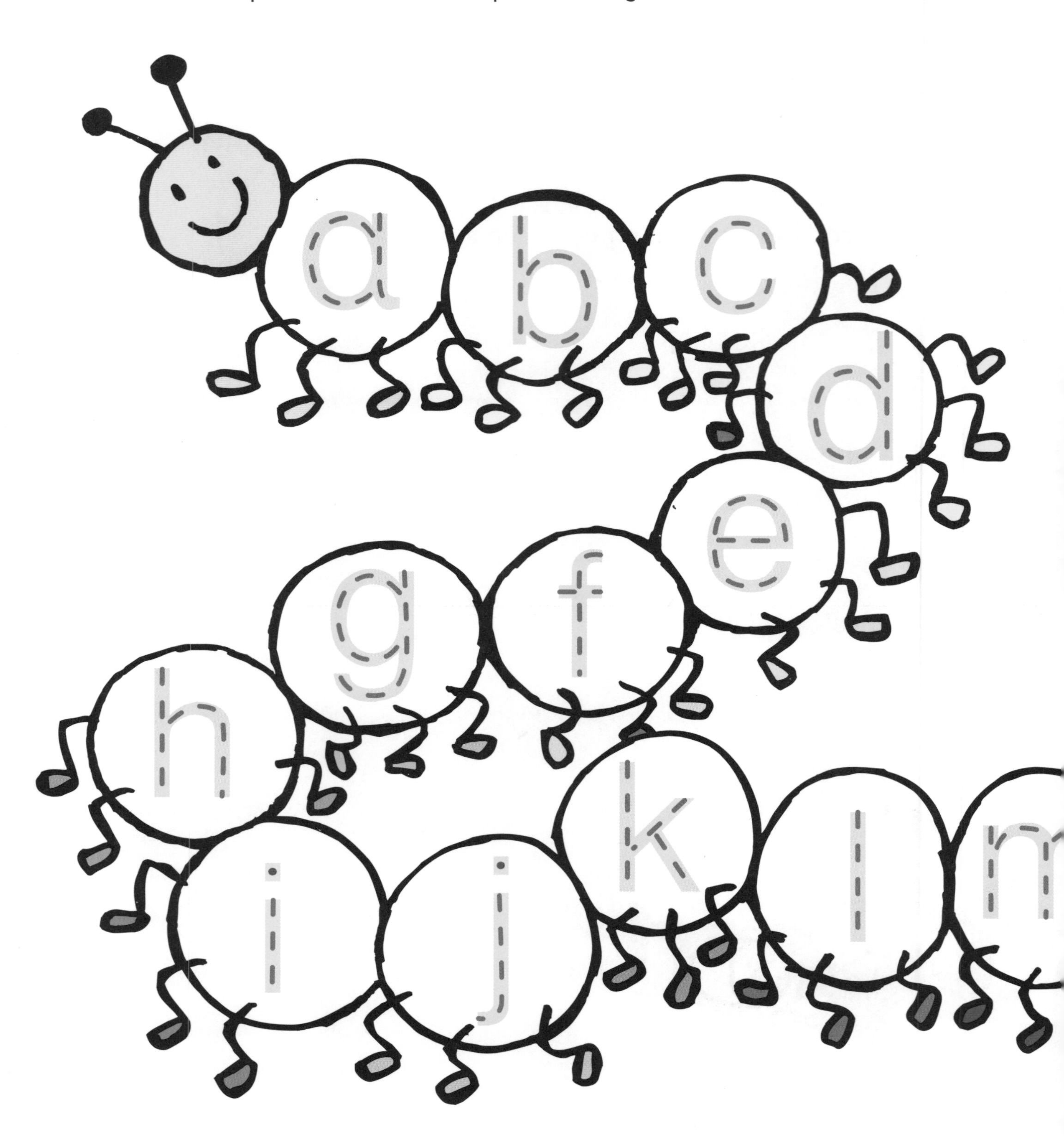

Write the alphabet

Colour the different letters that appear in your name.

Words I have learnt

Numbers:
one two three four five

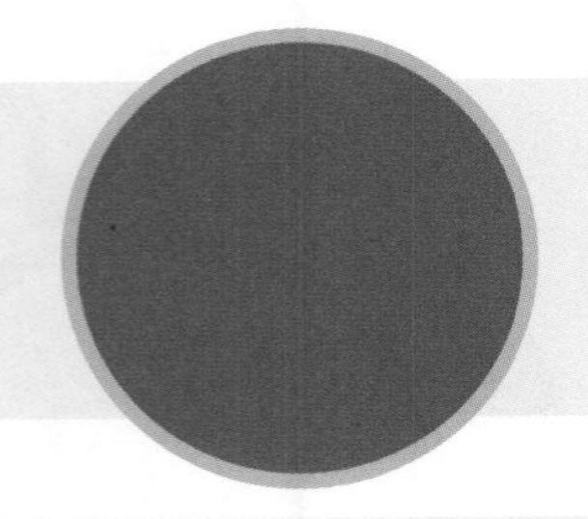

Colours:
blue green red yellow

People:
baby boy dad girl mum

Animals:
cat cow dog duck fish frog horse
insect penguin pig sheep zebra

Other nouns:
apple ball bed book car cup egg
gate jam jelly key king log moon
nest orange pan queen ring rug
sun table umbrella vase window
x as in box yo-yo

Connecting words: a and in is it on the

Tick the boxes to show what you know!

Now I can ...

- ☐ hold a pencil correctly
- ☐ draw straight lines going down
- ☐ draw straight lines going up
- ☐ draw straight lines going across
- ☐ draw curved lines
- ☐ draw diagonal lines
- ☐ draw circles
- ☐ see details in pictures
- ☐ tell a story
- ☐ say the sounds of all the letters, e.g. for b the letter sound is buh
- ☐ say the names of all the letters, e.g. for b the letter name is bee
- ☐ match pictures and letters
- ☐ identify letter shapes
- ☐ see the differences in letter shapes, e.g. b and d, m and n.
- ☐ begin to write the letters
- ☐ match pictures and words
- ☐ read 10 simple words from this book
- ☐ read 20 simple words from this book

You can learn with
I Can Learn
The best-selling I Can Learn series is the perfect introduction to learning at home.
Ages 3-4
Count to 10
Get Ready for Maths
I Can Read Letters
Match and Sort
Get Ready for Reading
Get Ready for Writing
Just £3.9
Ages 4-5
Count to 20
Fun with Phonics
I Can Read Words
I Can Write
Learn the Time
Simple Sums
Ages 5-6
Add and Subtract
Maths
Reading
Times Tables
Writing
Spelling
Ages 6-7
Add and Subtract
Handwriting
Maths
Reading
Spelling
Times Tables
Look out for more I Can Learn Megas!
Mega English
Mega English
Mega English
Mega Maths
Mega Maths
Mega Maths
Only £4.9
www.egmont.co.uk/icanlearn